SIR ISAAC NEWTON

PROFESSOR EDWARD NEVILLE DA COSTA ANDRADE was born in 1887 and educated at St. Dunstan's College, University College (London), the University of Heidelberg, Cavendish Laboratory (Cambridge), and the University of Manchester. His books include *The Structure of the Atom*, *The Mechanism of Nature* (with Julian Huxley), *Simple Science*, *The New Chemistry*, *The Atom and Its Energy*, *Poems and Songs*, *An Approach to Modern Physics;* he has written as well numerous articles for various technical journals and the Encyclopaedia Britannica.

Professor Andrade's latest book, *Rutherford and the Nature of the Atom*, is volume S35 of the Science Study Series. It was published in 1964.

Sir Isaac Newton

by

E. N. da C. Andrade

SCIENCE
STUDY
SERIES

Published by Anchor Books
Doubleday & Company, Inc.
Garden City, New York

TYPOGRAPHY BY EDWARD GOREY

Reprinted through the courtesy of The Macmillan Company, New York, and W. Collins Sons & Co., Ltd., London. First published 1954. All rights reserved. Printed in the United States of America.

THE SCIENCE STUDY SERIES

The Science Study Series offers to students and to the general public the writing of distinguished authors on the most stirring and fundamental topics of science, from the smallest known particles to the whole universe. Some of the books tell of the role of science in the world of man, his technology and civilization. Others are biographical in nature, telling the fascinating stories of the great discoverers and their discoveries. All the authors have been selected both for expertness in the fields they discuss and for ability to communicate their special knowledge and their own views in an interesting way. The primary purpose of these books is to provide a survey within the grasp of the young student or the layman. Many of the books, it is hoped, will encourage the reader to make his own investigations of natural phenomena.

The Series, which now offers topics in all the sciences and their applications, had its beginning in a project to revise the secondary schools' physics curriculum. At the Massachusetts Institute of Technology during 1956 a group of physicists, high school teachers, journalists, apparatus designers, film producers, and other specialists organized the Physical Science Study Committee, now operating as a part of Educational Services Incorporated, Watertown, Massachusetts. They pooled their knowledge and experience toward the design and creation of aids to the learning of physics. Initially their effort was supported by the National Science Foundation, which has continued to aid the program. The Ford Foundation, the Fund for the Advancement of Education, and the Alfred P. Sloan Foundation have also given support. The Committee has created a textbook, an extensive film series, a laboratory guide, especially designed apparatus, and a teachers' source book.

The Series is guided by a Board of Editors:
Bruce F. Kingsbury, Managing Editor
John H. Durston, General Editor

and Paul F. Brandwein, the Conservation Foundation and Harcourt, Brace & World, Inc.; Samuel A. Goudsmit, Brookhaven National Laboratory; Philippe LeCorbeiller, Harvard University; and Gerard Piel, *Scientific American*.

Acknowledgments

I am deeply grateful to Sir Harold Spencer Jones, the Astronomer Royal, for having given me the benefit of his vast knowledge on certain astronomical questions which arose, not necessarily for printing, while I was writing this book and to Dr. Sherwood Taylor for having put at my disposal his deep learning on alchemical matters.

PREFACE

I am naturally gratified that my little book on Isaac Newton has been included in the famous Science Study Series. This inclusion is, no doubt, a small manifestation of the increased interest in the mighty genius that has taken place since the Royal Society of London celebrated the three hundredth anniversary of his birth in 1942 and, wartime conditions having limited attendance in that year, again in 1946.

Evidence of this active interest is afforded by the studies in progress in the United States, in particular the significant work of Professor Bernard Cohen, of Harvard, whose edition of Isaac Newton's *Papers & Letters on Natural Philosophy* appeared in 1958 and whose critical edition of Newton's *Principia,* an undertaking involving prolonged study, is in active preparation.

Unpublished Scientific Papers of Isaac Newton, by A. R. Hall and M. B. Hall, a work of much importance, appeared in 1962. *The Correspondence of Isaac Newton,* in several volumes, is in the course of publication under the patronage of the Royal Society of London. The learned labors of D. T. Whiteside, at the University of Cambridge, are devoted to the editing of Newton's mathematical works, the first volume having appeared in 1964. In France Professor Koyré has given expert attention to Newtonian matters. These works are typical of the intensive study devoted in recent years to Isaac Newton: many distinguished scholars not cited are concerned with like matters.

The progress of exact science to its present height and scope, so far exceeding the bounds which seemed set even sixty years ago, has in no way diminished the esteem, the reverence, in which Newton's performance is held by all those versed in the history of the subject. The chief among those who have brought about the revolution in scientific ideas. Einstein, who showed, as everybody knows, that Newton's mechanics and physics had limitations, wrote of Newton's work in terms of the highest praise; A. S. Eddington, a great leader in the abstruse world of modern astronomy, writing of the new conceptions of space, time, and gravitation, said "To suppose that Newton's great scientific reputation is tossing up and down on these latter-day revolutions is to confuse science with omniscience."

On the statue of Newton which stands in the chapel of Trinity College, Cambridge, are engraved words of the Latin poet Lucretius which, translated, read "who excelled the human race in power of thought." If this little book should in any way make clear to the general reader that this tribute is a just one, I shall be a happy man.

E. N. DA C. ANDRADE

CONTENTS

DIAGRAMS

SIR ISAAC NEWTON

I

Science Before Newton

ISAAC NEWTON is one of the greatest names in the history of human thought. Wherever the development of science is studied, wherever men set out to consider seriously the way in which modern views and methods of scientific search developed, he is held in reverence, in Russia as in the United States, in Germany as in Great Britain. Nearly everyone who takes any interest in history, in science or in serious affairs in general has heard of him and realises that he is an outstanding man, but few, perhaps, understand, even in a general way, why it is that he is famous. It is the object of this little book to say something of Newton's life and times, but in particular to make clear what it was that he did and why it was of such great importance for the development of scientific thought.

The only things that are usually told of him are, firstly, that he saw an apple fall and that this led him to the conclusion that it fell because the earth attracted it and, secondly, that he discovered that a prism split up white light into coloured light. But long before Newton men had considered fall as due to the pull of the earth and this supposition is not, surely, a very striking scientific advance towards understanding how the material universe works. Again, when Newton first bought a prism he said that he did so to try the "celebrated phenomena of colours," so that the fact that a prism produced light of all colours was well known before him and is, after all, not in itself a very important observation. As a matter of fact Seneca wrote of it in the first century A.D.

A very important part of Newton's work was, it is true, concerned with the pull of gravity and with the passage of light through a prism, but the profound significance of this work is not clear without some knowledge of its nature and of the times when it was carried out. It meant a new way of looking at the facts of observation and the problems of science, the passage from old methods of approach and old traditions to modern ways of scientific thought. To understand the great consequences of Newton's discoveries for the development of science we must consider the position of science and learning in the world into which he was born in 1642. You may say that it should be, rather, the world as he found it when a young man, but things did not change much in twenty years in those days. In fact, when he died in 1727 certain theories which he had shown to be quite unsound were still being taught.

Newton, of course, did not stand alone. He was the greatest of many men who were in those times building the foundations of modern science, but he was not the only one. The spirit of experimental science was in the air: Newton was the supreme figure of an intellectual movement then in progress. Great men do not occur in mental and spiritual isolation from their times. Michelangelo, supreme of the Florentine artists of the Renaissance, worked in a period when there was a mighty flowering of art in Italy, when artists of genius abounded there. Shakespeare is the greatest dramatist, but in the Elizabethan age when he flourished the stage was a centre of lively interest and activity for men of action and writers alike, and there were dozens of lesser playwrights, some of them second only to Shakespeare. Men of all classes loved plays and poetry. The age of Beethoven was an age of great music: he was mightiest among many great musicians who were passionately active at his time. In Newton's time, then, there were many signs of a scientific stirring, of the vigorous sprouting of the experimental method. Scientific societies were arising: the Accademia del Cimento, that is, the Academy of Experiment, was founded in Italy in 1657 and, although it did not last very long, was responsible for much important work: the Royal Society, of which we shall have much to say, was founded in 1660, when Newton was still at school. The first scientific periodicals appeared in England and France a few years later. In speaking, then, of the world of science as Newton found it and as he left it, I am not suggesting that there was a sudden change due to him alone. Rather, there was a wide forward movement, with many leaders, but with one supreme genius, Newton: with much fundamental work, of which his is the superlative type; with many striking advances made with limited aims and objectives, but with one man, Newton, possessed of a general comprehensive plan, clear, confident and certain.

Let us look now at the world of learning round about 1650. The works of the philosophers of ancient Greece had immense authority at the universities of all countries and with learned men in general. Aristotle, whose works had been rediscovered and translated into Latin between 1200 and 1225, was, in particular, one to whom they turned when they wanted the answer to difficult questions in the sciences of the day, especially questions of movement, of bodies on earth and of the heavenly bodies, just as they turned to Euclid and the other Greek geometers in matters of mathematics and to Plato and others in matters of pure philosophy. The works of Aristotle were a kind of encyclopædia of the knowledge of the ancient world and many thought that to refer to them was the best and surest way of finding out the method and reason of material happenings. Quite a number of writers believed that the intelligence of the world had declined since the days of the great Greeks, so that they represented the most reliable source of knowledge.

Now Aristotle and the other Greek thinkers who dealt with motion on earth and in the heavens, with light, sound and other subjects of what was called natural philosophy, were accustomed to seek the solution of their problems by speculating, by meditating, by pondering rather than by experiment, observation or measurement. They started with certain philosophical ideas as to the nature of things, which they derived by intense thought and they proceeded from these ideas by arguing, very acutely, according to certain rules. They considered that knowledge about nature could be won by pure thought, and that experiment was, in a way, a rather trivial and pedestrian proceeding, with which a thinker need not much concern himself, in fact

which might be misleading. The properties of
numbers were, for instance, a matter with which
a philosopher might well occupy himself, but
pushing and pulling things, letting them fall and
timing them, was not, they thought, the way to
find out about motion. This may seem strange,
but the great Galileo, being brought up in the
Aristotelian tradition, wrote after certain of his
early experiments, "but we will work more with
reasoning than with examples, for what we seek
is the cause of phenomena, which experiment
does not provide." Later he carried out, and
relied on, most important experiments. The
Greek philosophers were seeking for causes:
they wanted to get to the bottom of things, to
know what matter was and why it behaved as
it does. This is not the same thing as wanting
to know the rules that govern the way in which
things behave. Why there is a heaven and an
earth, what is the nature of man's being, what
is the cause of gravity—these are quite different
questions from why there is an eclipse of the
sun, meaning how to calculate when the moon
will pass between sun and earth; why man needs
to breathe, meaning how the oxygen of the air
behaves in the lungs; what is the cause of the
tides, meaning how to calculate tidal behaviour
from the pull of the sun and moon.

For instance, those brought up in the Aristotelian way of thinking asked what light was, was

it a substance or something philosophically different. This made it necessary to discuss exactly what was meant by a substance and what other possibilities existed, a matter which gave abundant scope for skilful argument, but not much possibility of reaching any decision of scientific interest. As we shall see later, this was just the kind of question that Newton refused to discuss: he sought to find out how light behaved.

As regards the science of light, as we understand it, the Greeks of antiquity knew that light travelled in straight lines and also the simple laws of reflection, so that they were able to work out by geometry, in which they excelled, problems dealing with shadows and mirrors. They knew nothing of lenses, which were first used as spectacles round about 1300 and were combined to make a telescope soon after 1600. Galileo, who died in 1642, the year in which Newton was born, was the first man to use the telescope to study the heavens and made striking discoveries with it. Kepler, who discovered the laws of the motions of the planets, wrote an important book dealing with how to combine lenses to make a telescope. Primitive microscopes came a little later. So the science of optics had made some progress before Newton's time and simple optical instruments had been invented, but of the nature of colour nothing was known, although it was much discussed in terms of philosophy. The disputants agreed that white light was simple and that colour was a complication. Newton was to prove experimentally that this was quite wrong.

The subject of mechanics was one on which Aristotle and his followers had written at length and his methods and conclusions were widely taught when Newton was a young man, although Galileo had shown that in some respects, at any rate, they were quite wrong. Aristotle distinguished, in a debating manner, between natural and non-natural motions. From the movements of the heavenly bodies he concluded that motion in a circle was a form of natural motion. Since a stone when dropped moved by itself in a vertical line, he concluded that vertical motion in a straight line was natural. The motion of a pushed or pulled body, which was provoked from outside, was non-natural, he thought, because it required an active force to keep it going. Now a body pulled or pushed over the ground stops, in general, when the force acting on it stops: from this Aristotle concluded that a body in non-natural motion moved only if a force was acting on it. Once this was decided, he had to suppose that some force acted on a thrown stone after it left the hand, to keep it in motion, and he further concluded that the air beat on it behind and urged it forward. Aristotle was generalising from

the fact that any body which is moving comes
to rest if left to itself, but, mighty intellect though
he was, he generalised wrongly.

Suppose that we consider a truck or carriage
with very well-oiled wheels on a smooth sheet
of ice or on very well-laid horizontal rails. If it
is given a push it will go a long way before it
stops. The correct generalisation is that it would
go on for ever if it were not for the small forces
of friction which act so as to oppose the motion. A body travelling in a straight line at a
certain speed goes on for ever in the same line
at the same speed if no force acts on it. The
thrown body goes in a curved path because the
force of gravity pulls it down. A body at rest
stays at rest if no force acts on it. This tendency
to persist in a straight line motion or at rest is
called inertia. Kepler, as we shall see, had no
notion of it: he thought, as did Aristotle, that
to keep a body moving required a force acting
all the time. Galileo was the first man to have
clear notions about inertia: he understood that
the path of a thrown body was made up of a
steady horizontal travel at a uniform speed generally combined with a vertical motion upwards
which was diminished by, and ultimately over-
come by, gravity. He was not, however, at all
clear as to the general laws of motion. It was
Newton who first set down these general laws
with precision and showed what followed from

them, but he found the work of Galileo as a starting point. How little notion Galileo had of universal gravitation is shown by the fact that he spoke of stones being dropped from the moon so as to fall upon the earth.

One of Newton's greatest achievements was to explain the motion of the heavenly bodies on the basis of the laws of motion and of universal gravitation, that is, on the basis of laws that held throughout the universe, which, of course, meant that they held for bodies in motion on the earth. The mere notion that the same laws governed the movement of earthly and heavenly bodies was in itself quite against the ideas of those before him, although in his time others, such as Robert Hooke, Edmond Halley and Christopher Wren were becoming convinced of it. Aristotle, however, and his followers thought of the heavenly bodies as obeying laws quite different from those that held on earth. These bodies were, they believed, of a divine, immortal and perfect nature, unlike things terrestrial that were mortal and subject to change and decay. For instance, when sun-spots were discovered by Galileo and others, those who believed in the conventional teaching denied that they could exist, because the sun, the eye of the world, was perfect and so could not have spots on it: they did not look, they knew. When a new star appeared in the constellation of Serpentarius in 1604 the Aristotelians were loath to believe in it, because the heavens, being perfect, were not subject to innovation. The circular motion of the stars showed that circular motion had in it something perfect, harmonious and natural. Astronomy plays so great a part in Newton's work that it may be well to consider very briefly the history of the subject up to his time.

Astronomy must be the oldest of the sciences, for as soon as man had learnt to think about what he saw around him the regularities of the motions of the celestial bodies must have impressed him and called for study. The regular movements of the moon constitute a kind of thirty-day clock: our word *month* is only a form of *mooneth*. Agriculture led to a study of the seasons and the sun's apparent motion. Certain groups of stars, such as the Great Bear, Casseopeia's Chair and Orion must strike anybody who looks at the heavens at night and very early in the history of civilisation it must have become familiar that they kept their positions in relation to one another and, with the other stars, travelled round as if painted on the inside of a great sphere with the earth at the centre. Their motions were, in fact, explained by supposing that they were attached, in some way, to a celestial sphere rotating about an axis through the earth.

This was easy: the difficult problem was to explain the motions of the planets, the wanderers —for the Greek word *planetes* means "a wanderer"—which did not move with the sphere, but strayed through the starry field, each planet being at one time in one constellation and at another time in another. The paths of all the planets lie in a narrow belt among the stars, the zodiac, nearly in one plane, which also includes the sun and the earth. The five planets, visible to the naked eye, which were known to the ancients were Mercury, Venus, Mars, Jupiter and Saturn. Since Newton's time three more major planets have been discovered by the application of Newtonian methods and the aid of powerful telescopes—Uranus, Neptune and Pluto, as well as a host of comparatively very small planets called "minor planets" or "asteroids." The largest of these is Ceres, whose diameter is about a fifth of that of the moon, but it is not a very conspicuous object, since it is getting on for a thousand times as far off. The ancients, who believed that the earth was fixed, considered the sun and the moon as planets, making seven planets in all, and in the middle ages and even later the number seven was considered to have a mystic significance. When Galileo discovered with the telescope the satellites of Jupiter a Florentine astronomer proved that they could not exist in the following way: "There are seven windows given to animals through which the air is admitted to the tabernacle of the body, to enlighten, to warm and to nourish it. What are these parts of the microcosmos? Two nostrils, two eyes, two ears and a mouth. So in the heavens, as in a macrocosmos, there are two favourable stars, two unpropitious, two luminaries and Mercury undecided and indifferent. From this and many other similarities in nature, such as the seven metals, et cetera, which it were tedious to enumerate, we gather that the number of planets is necessarily seven. Moreover, these satellites of Jupiter are invisible to the naked eye and therefore would be useless and therefore do not exist. Besides the Jews and other ancient nations, as well as modern Europeans, have adopted the division of the week into seven days and have named them after the seven planets. Now if we increase the number of planets, this whole and beautiful system falls to the ground."

This was printed in a book on astronomy published thirty-one years before Newton was born. It is an extreme case, but something of this kind of argument persisted in Newton's time.

Other heavenly bodies, besides the stars and the planets, whose motion came up for consideration by Newton, were the comets, bright bodies with luminous tails which from time to time came near enough to the earth to be seen by the naked eye. They appeared without any warning, remained visible for a few weeks or so and then faded away. From earliest times they excited great wonder and were generally believed to foretell some stirring events in those days, when men's lives were supposed to be governed by the planets and the heavenly bodies in general. Thus in Shakespeare's *Julius Cæsar* Calpurnia says

When beggars die there are no comets seen
The heavens themselves blaze forth the death of
*   princes*

and in *King Henry VI, First Part,* Bedford declaims

Comets, importing change of times and states
Brandish your crystal tresses in the sky . . .

One of Newton's feats which particularly impressed men of his time was to show that the behaviour of comets was not erratic, but that they obeyed the law of gravitation and that their orbits were subject to accurate calculation. A brilliant comet which appeared in 1680, to the path of which he applied his principles, is often represented in contemporary engravings and images of Newton, for instance on a Staffordshire ware figure of him.

The planets presented a great problem to the ancients because of certain peculiarities of their motion as seen against the background of the

stars. They do not move steadily round in one
direction, from east to west, against this background, but at certain stages of their progress
appear to stop momentarily and then move from
west to east in a backward or "retrograde" motion, as it is called, and in due course stop momentarily and then proceed forward again. The
Greeks developed a detailed system of astronomy which reigned undisputed until a hundred
years or so before Newton and which was still
widely accepted until his day. It is usually as-
sociated with the name of Ptolemy, who lived in
Alexandria in Egypt from about A.D. 90 to 168.
Here he taught astronomy and wrote the books
which were to be studied for centuries. The
chief of these books is usually known by the
Arabic title, *Almagest,* for it was the Arabs
who kept learning alive during the dark ages.
Ptolemy taught that the earth was at rest and
that the stars were fixed to a great sphere rotating round the earth, which, of course, explained
quite well their apparent motions. The sun,
moon and planets were supposed to move in
connection with different spheres, one each,
surrounding the earth, but since, as has been
said, they did not move steadily in circles, other
circular motions were introduced. If a body is
carried by a rotating circle whose centre moves
on another circle, things can be so arranged, by
adjusting size and speed, that it carries out a

retrograde motion at intervals. A foot on a bicycle pedal goes forward at the top of the stroke and backwards at the bottom: if the gearing were so arranged that several revolutions of the pedal were necessary to produce one revolution of the bicycle wheel the foot would be actually going backwards, relative to the ground, at the bottom of the stroke. This analogy with planetary motion is not very close: it is designed only to show in a general way how motion in a moving circle can lead to retrograde motion. A point moving in a circle, the centre of which travels on a larger circle, is said to describe an epicycle. The system of Ptolemy was a very complicated one, but all that we need to remember, for our purpose, is that the earth was supposed, as seemed natural, to be at rest; that circular motion was supposed to have something perfect and celestial which rendered it alone proper for the representation of heavenly motions and that an elaborate system of circular motions could be made to give a rough, but not very close, representation of the motions of the planets. Milton, who knew of this classical astronomy and of the difficulties which it met, refers to these attempts to picture the planetary motions.

> *how will they wield*
> *The mighty frame, how build, unbuild, contrive*

To save appearances, how gird the sphere
With centric and eccentric scribbed o'er,
Cycle and epicycle, orb in orb.

which really gives a very good notion of the
Ptolemaic system.

It was some fourteen hundred years later that
Copernicus,[1] in 1530, put forward a completely
new notion of the movements of the heavenly
bodies. He maintained that it was much simpler
to understand these movements if we supposed
that the sun and the stars stood still, and the
earth went round the sun in the course of a year,
and turned on its own axis, which was tilted to
the plane of its path, in the course of a day.
Actually a Greek, Aristarchus, had put this forward nearly eighteen hundred years earlier, but
he had been forgotten. Copernicus, however,
went much further: he said that the earth was
a planet like the other planets, which all went
round the sun in circular paths. That is, he did
not, like his contemporaries, regard the sun as
a planet, but as the centre of the universe: further, he was clear that the moon circled round

[1] His real name was Koppernigk, but it was
usual in these times for a learned man to adopt a
Latin version of his name, or sometimes even a
Latin translation. Thus Bauer, whose name means
'peasant' in German, called himself Agricola,
which is the Latin for the word, and a Schmidt
(that is, Smith) of about the same period, called
himself Faber, Latin for blacksmith.

the earth as a satellite. In distance from the sun the order of the planets was as follows: Mercury, Venus, Earth, Mars, Jupiter, Saturn. The time taken for a planet to go once round in its orbit is greater the greater the orbit, so that a planet that is on a line from the sun through the earth at a particular moment will not remain in line. The earth is not at the centre of the planetary orbits: consequently we see celestial things, roughly speaking, first from one side and then from the other, which accounts for the fact that the motions of the planets appear irregular to us, and retrograde at intervals although they are actually moving steadily round.[2] The stars are so distant that this varying viewpoint makes no difference as far as they are concerned.

This placing the sun at the centre of the planetary system, and considering the earth as a planet, made things much simpler, but these steady motions in circular orbits did not quite fit with the observations—and the whole object of the exact sciences is to fit not the general way, but the precise way, expressed in numbers, in which things happen. Copernicus found that to account for the positions and time-tables of the

---

[2] For those who would like to follow this up—it is in no way essential to the book and can be left alone without hurt to the story of Newton—the note at the end of the book may make the matter clearer.

planets, as measured by the astronomers, he had
to put the centre of his circles not just in the sun,
but a bit to one side, which rather spoilt the sim-
plicity, and even then the fit was not exact.
Things were actually more complicated than
appears in the simple diagram (Fig. 1) when it

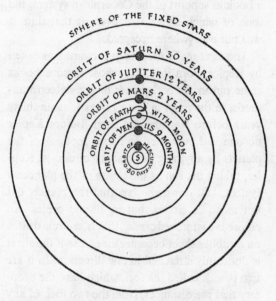

*Fig. 1. A simple representation of the system
of Copernicus, as given in his book in 1530.
The sizes of the orbits are not to scale, for actually the orbit of Saturn, for instance, is
about 24 times that of Mercury, and 9½
times that of the earth. The times shown for
once round the orbit are the rough values
given by Copernicus, not the modern values*

19

came to details and not much notice was taken by contemporary astronomers of the book in which Copernicus expressed his scheme. It appeared in 1543 when he was on his death bed, so that he was not there to support his views. About a hundred years later John Wilkins wrote a book in support of the Copernican system, the tone of which shows that even at that time it was not everywhere accepted.

The next really great step forward was taken by Kepler, born in 1571, whose famous books came out in the early years of the sixteen hundreds, in the reign of King James I, some thirty years before Newton was born. Before Kepler no one had ever tried to fit the motions of the planets by anything but systems of circles. Kepler, taking the sun as the centre of the planetary system, laid down the law that the planets did not move in circles, but in elliptic orbits. An ellipse is a stretched circle: that is, a circle drawn on a rubber sheet becomes an ellipse if the sheet is uniformly stretched in one direction. In it are two points, called the foci, which have the property that the distances, from the two foci, of any point on the ellipse add up to the same value whatever point on the ellipse be taken. The shadow of a ball on a sheet of card held obliquely is of elliptic form.

Kepler's first law is that the orbits of the planets are ellipses with the sun as one focus:

the other focus is called the empty focus. Kepler further stated that the planets did not move at the same speed in all parts of the orbit, but faster as they neared the focus and in his second law he gave the rule for finding the speed at each point. This law says that the rate at which the line joining the planet to the sun sweeps out

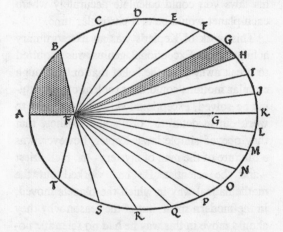

Fig. 2. An elliptic orbit, showing the positions, indicated by letters, of a planet at equal intervals of time. The positions have been calculated so as to make the area between the lines joining F to two following positions of the planet the same in all cases, according to Kepler's second law. Thus, shaded area FAB equals shaded area FGH. It is clear that the nearer the planet to the Sun, the faster it goes. The actual ellipses of planetary orbits are much closer to circles than that shown in the diagram. G is the empty focus

the area is the same all through the orbit (see Fig. 2). His third law laid down how the time for once round the orbit, the planet's year, depended upon the size of the orbit: the square of the year is proportional to the cube of the orbit. Thus what Kepler did was to give an exact time-table of the planetary motions: from his laws you could calculate accurately where each planet would be at a particular time.

This work of Kepler's was an extraordinary achievement. Exceptional genius was required to break away from the belief that only through circular motions could the problem of the planets be solved, exceptional skill and industry to work out in detail the orbits and to show that they obeyed simple laws. Kepler, however, was a mixture of the man of mystery—the high priest —and the scientist. He had worked out the mathematical way in which the planets moved, in the modern spirit, but of the reason why they should move in this way he had no scientific notion. He believed, like the Aristotelians, that a body could not keep moving unless it was pushed all the time and thought that some moving spirits must urge the planets on. Later he thought that some peculiar kind of magnetic force (nothing like the ordinary magnetic force) might possibly do the pushing. He either believed in or pretended to believe in, astrology, the doctrine that men's lives are governed by the heavenly bodies and can be foretold by the positions of the stars and planets at the time of their birth. He cast the horoscopes of famous men, which was a way of making money. In fact he said that without the daughter astrology the mother astronomy must have starved.

There is another outstanding figure whom we must mention in connection with the problem of the motion of the planets, and that is the Frenchman Descartes, who died seven years after Newton's birth. He was not only a great philosopher but a great mathematician. Strangely enough, however, he did not apply mathematical methods to his considerations of the motions of a heavenly body. Starting rather with certain philosophical principles, he put forward a system of the universe which was accepted by most of the learned men of his time and long after. He supposed that the whole of the space of the heavens was filled with very fine invisible particles, which moved round in great vortices, or whirlpools. One vortex was centred on the sun: the swarms of particles careering round the sun dragged the planets with them. A minor vortex of particles round the earth dragged the moon along. This theory of vortices gave a picture of the working of the heavens which could be drawn and was easy to understand, but, of course, it gave no explanation of why the planets moved in ellipses, why the planets nearer the sun had shorter years than the remote ones, or, indeed, of any of the numerical laws of the heavens. From the viewpoint of the science of to-day it took us no further than just saying that the planets obeyed Kepler's law because that was how things were bound to happen. This, then, was the position of astronomy as Newton found it. Kepler's laws gave very accurately the planetary time-table, but no celestial mechanics to account for these laws: Descartes' vortices gave the kind of pictorial explanation that might serve in a general discussion when nobody was worrying about measurement, but there had been no suggestion of any kind of mechanical laws that would account mathematically for the behaviour of the planets.

The position of science in other matters in which Newton made fundamental discoveries we can deal with when we come to describe those discoveries. Now that we have some notion of the kind of world and the kind of learning into which he was born, let us turn to Newton himself.

II

He Goes to Cambridge

NEWTON WAS a country boy, born on Christmas day, 1642, in a small stone-built farm-house standing near the village of Colsterworth in Lincolnshire. The nearest place of any size and importance was Grantham, a town then of some two or three thousand inhabitants. The house was called the Manor House of Woolsthorpe, but I have said 'farm-house' because it was used as such, for Newton's father and ancestors were yeoman farmers. The house still stands for the visitor to see.

Newton's father died before his famous child was born, and the baby was a very small and weakly one. Newton used to tell of his mother's saying that at the time of his birth he might have been put in a quart mug and for some time a kind of bolster was placed round his neck to support his head, as he was too weak to hold it aright. However, he grew up to be a healthy lad and after attending two little day schools, which were near enough to his home for him to walk there and back daily, was sent at the age of twelve to the King's School in Grantham, which was distant about seven miles. The daily journey was therefore too much, so during term time he lodged in the town with an apothecary named Clark, who seems to have been very kind to him and, in particular, to have encouraged him in making things with his hands, which Newton loved to do. We have many tales of Newton's schooldays, set down years afterwards when he was famous. While he was at school a windmill was built near Grantham, which was somewhat of a rarity in that part of the country, since rivers and brooks are in plenty there and people used water-wheels to drive their millstones for grinding the corn. Newton made an exact model of this windmill, and his model seems, by all accounts, to have worked in the wind. He made water clocks, one of which was kept going by water dripping out of a cistern: in consequence a board floating on the water slowly moved downwards and, as it moved turned an hour hand by means of a string passing over a wheel. It is said to have been a good timekeeper, but in those days they did not trouble greatly about odd minutes, or even quarter hours. We know that he found a description of a water clock of this and other kinds in a book called *The Mysteries of Art and Nature,* by John Bate, which contains directions for making various simple machines, for making fireworks, for drawing and painting, as well as hints on handicrafts and medical recipes—a good boy's book. This must have been favourite reading with young Newton, for we have a notebook of his in which he copied out pages of the hints on drawing and on how to make colours for painting, as well as such things as "A bait to catch fish," "To make birds drunk" and accounts of a few simple conjuring tricks.

The boy was very fond of copying drawings from books. He cut a sundial on one of the building stones in the side of his home[1] and made other sundials of various kinds, which required good knowledge. He also cut his name all over the place at school: as a friend of his later years, Dr. William Stukeley, wrote "I have heard likewise at Grantham school that before the present seats and desks were set up, he had cut his name, upon the old ones, in all the places where he had sat, in his several removes." Kites, lanterns, dolls' furniture, he made them all: he even made a wheeled chair for himself. There is no doubt, then, that he had a passionate liking

[1] This stone is now in the possession of the Royal Society.

for handicrafts of all kinds, for drawing and for copying bits out of books, but there is nothing in all this to suggest exceptional genius, any more than there is in his fondness for flowers and collecting herbs. There have been great men who while still of school age have shown extraordinary mental powers. Blaise Pascal by the time he was sixteen years of age had completed a book on conic sections which contained important new discoveries, including "Pascal's hexagon," well known to students of geometry. Evariste Galois, famous for great discoveries in mathematics, was killed at the age of twenty in a duel about a worthless woman whom he knew to be worthless. William Rowan Hamilton, likewise known for his fundamental mathematical researches, at fourteen had a good knowledge of Hebrew, Latin, Greek, Syriac, Persian, Sanskrit, Hindustani and Malay and even wrote a letter to the Persian ambassador in his own language, and at sixteen showed his mathematical genius by discovering an error in an abstruse mathematical work on astronomy and by writing an original paper on the properties of certain curves. When he was eighteen the Royal Astronomer of Ireland remarked of him: "This young man, I do not say *will be,* but *is,* the first mathematician of his age." James Clerk Maxwell, whose mathematical work led to the discovery of "wireless" waves, wrote an original mathematical paper which was published by the Royal Society of Edinburgh when he was barely fifteen. These men, then, showed early that they were of quite outstanding intellect. There was nothing of this kind about young Newton. Probably the most that anyone could have said of him was that he was a bright boy, with a real gift for making models and drawing.

As regards his character as a schoolboy, various stories have come down to us. One, illustrating his courage and determination, is that when he was in a low form at the Grantham school, a boy gave him a painful kick. "When school was over," says the narrator, "Newton challenged him to fight, and they went into the churchyard. While they were fighting, the Master's son came out and encouraged them by clapping one on the back and winking at the other" (this reads as if the story were strictly true). "Isaac Newton had the more spirit and resolution, and beat him until he would fight no more. Young Stokes (that is, the Master's son) told Isaac Newton to treat him like a coward and rub his nose against the wall, and accordingly Isaac Newton pulled him along by the ears and thrust his face against the side of the church. Determined to beat him also at his books, by hard work he finally succeeded, and then gradually rose to be the first in the school."

There are other tales which refer to his absent-mindedness: how, for instance, going home from Grantham it was usual to dismount and lead one's horse up a particularly steep hill. On one occasion Newton did this but forgot to remount and led his horse the whole way home. On another occasion the horse, while being led, slipped its bridle and went home by itself, while Newton walked on with the bridle without noticing anything strange. Even if these stories were a little exaggerated in the telling after Newton became famous, they probably had some basis and, with others of his growing love for books, help us to understand why his mother at last agreed with his old schoolmaster, Mr. Stokes, not to try to force him to be a farmer, for which he had little inclination and little fitness, but to let him go to the University. Accordingly we find him in 1661, at the age of eighteen, off to Cambridge, where he had been accepted at the famous and influential Trinity College. He had little money and became what was then called a Sizar, a student who paid his way through college by doing odd jobs and waiting on his tutor.

We know very little about his first two years there: all through his life he never sought company and probably as an undergraduate of very sober tastes and rigid morals he mixed little with his rather rowdy and wealthier fellow students. When he was about twenty-one, however, he came into contact with Isaac Barrow, who was what was called Lucasian Professor of Mathematics in the University, so named after Henry Lucas who originally provided the money to found the professorship.[2] Barrow was a very gifted mathematician, as well as a classical scholar and a great divine and preacher. He soon recognised that the young man was something quite out of the way as a scientist, or "natural philosopher," as they said then, for the word "scientist" was not used before 1840. He encouraged him in his mathematical studies and directed his attention to optics. Later in 1669, when Barrow published his book on optics, he had such trust in Newton that he turned to him for help, and in that same year Barrow resigned his post in favour of Newton, who became Lucasian Professor. But we have much to record before that.

It was in 1665 that Newton took his degree of B.A., without any particular distinction. Even in Cambridge, then, he could still be said to be a man, practically unknown except to Barrow. In that year a terrible thing happened. The Great Plague, which had started comparatively mildly in London the year before, became very severe: in July, August and September more

[2] The Lucasian Professor is still a famous title: at the time when I write this it is held by the celebrated mathematician Dirac.

than a tenth of the population of London died of it. In the autumn they became afraid of it in Cambridge and closed the University, the students returning to their homes. Newton went back to the little house of his birth at Woolsthorpe, where he spent most of his time until the University reopened again in the spring of 1667. He was, then, alone, as far as intellectual company goes, at Woolsthorpe for some eighteen months. We are very much in the dark as to what he had done before he went there; throughout his life Newton was very secretive about his work. We know, however, that when he returned to Cambridge he had already firmly laid the foundations of the work for which he will ever be famous: that he had accomplished extraordinary things brooding there alone. We will devote a new chapter to the great period of intense and concentrated thought at Woolsthorpe.

III

Meditations at Woolsthorpe

NEWTON, as we shall see, unlike most men of science, never showed any strong wish to publish his work, but rather the reverse. He had to be persuaded and coaxed to make the results of his labours known. He would work out things of the utmost importance and then put them aside among his papers. In consequence it is often not easy to find out what he did and when he did it, especially in this period before his first published work, which did not come out until he was twenty-nine. We have, therefore, to decide from various pieces of evidence what great discoveries Newton, pondering alone, alone in that small stone house set apart in the wide countryside, reached by intense and concentrated thought in his twenty-third and twenty-fourth year. We are brought to the conclusion that, in spite of his later extraordinary performances, these were, perhaps, the most fruitful years of his life. Here we are supported by Newton himself, for in his old age, writing a note on his early work at this time, he set down "All this was in the two plague years of 1665 and 1666, for in those days I was in the prime of my age for invention, and minded mathematics and philosophy more than at any time since." By "philosophy" he meant "natural philosophy," or science, as we should say now, so that in the language of to-day he was declaring that in those years his power of original work was at its highest and that he paid closer attention to mathematics and science then than at any time later.

I say that he was alone; I mean intellectually, without any one to talk to about what he was thinking, and without any correspondence with learned men. His mother was there: two years after the death of her first husband, Isaac Newton's father, she had married again and gone to live with her new husband, the Rev. Barnabas Smith, at the nearby village of North Witham, where he was rector, but he died when Newton was at school in Grantham and she had returned to Woolsthorpe, with three young children. Incidentally, Barnabas Smith had had Woolsthorpe Manor, which had fallen into serious disrepair, rebuilt, so that the house as we now know it is not quite the same as it was when

Newton was born there. Newton was always greatly attached to his mother: when, many years later, she was dying, he sat at her bedside night after night and himself applied the medical dressings that were necessary. It also appears that she was devoted to him. We may suppose, therefore, that he was well cared for by his mother and discussed with her, perhaps, the local and home affairs of the day, but most certainly not his scientific meditations.

Much later, when he was asked how he made his discoveries, he said, "By always thinking unto them," and on another occasion, when he seems to have been rather more talkative, "I keep the subject constantly before me and wait till the first dawnings open little by little into the full light." Even for great men of science it is hard to keep the mind concentrated on a problem, to the exclusion of everything else, for more than an hour or two: I believe that Newton, however, could sit for hours with the whole powers of his mind fixed on whatever difficulty he was concerned with. I imagine him, then, as sitting there at Woolsthorpe, perhaps in the orchard on a summer afternoon or in the kitchen on a winter's evening, completely ignorant of what was going on around him, pondering the motions of the heavenly bodies, or new mathematical methods, or the nature and behaviour of light.

His way of looking at things, the problems which he set himself, were new. Newton was convinced that the laws that governed the celestial motions were ordinary mechanical laws of some kind, such as governed the motion of bodies on earth. Before him, as we have seen, the general opinion in the learned world was that they had laws of their own; celestial perfection, spirits, mystery entered into the question. Isaac Newton was a devoutly religious man, and in many ways a mystic, but he did not believe that religion or mystery had anything to do with the mathematical laws of planetary motion, although they had to do with the First Cause. Late in his life he wrote, discussing the Creator at the end of his book *Opticks,* "Such a wonderful Uniformity in the Planetary System must be allowed the Effect of Choice," that is, it must be admitted to come about by design and not by chance. That was his belief throughout his life. But it is one thing to believe, say, that secret causes that we do not understand may have led a man to drive a motor car from London to York, and another thing to say that mysterious causes govern the workings of the internal combustion engine.

He thought about the moon's motion. A metal ball—or a chestnut—swinging in a circle on a string tends to fly off: the pull of it can be felt. If the string gives way, the ball moves away in a straight line in the direction in which it was moving at the moment of break. This kind of general statement was, of course, quite insufficient for Newton. He worked out exactly the inward pull that is required to keep a body, of a certain mass, moving with a certain speed, in a circle of a fixed radius. This inward pull is called the centrifugal force: centrifugal means "flying away from the centre," but, of course, the force that tends to take the body away from the centre is exactly equal to the inward force required to keep it from flying away. It is probable that Christian Huygens, the great Dutch scientist, had carried out this calculation earlier, for later in his life Newton wrote, "What Mr. Huygens has published since about centrifugal force I suppose he had before me," but he had not published at the time in question and Newton knew nothing of his work.

Convinced as he was that the moon obeyed the same laws as a moving body on the earth, his problem was to find out what force kept it from flying away, as any body moving in a circular path should do. This is where the apple comes in. As he sits by the apple tree at Woolsthorpe Newton's meditations are disturbed by the soft thud of an apple falling on the grass. He thinks of it as falling in consequence of the central pull of the earth and then—as far as we can make out—the thought suddenly comes to him, may not the earth, which pulls the apple, also pull the moon? May it not be this pull, suitably weakened by the great distance, that keeps the moon from flying out of its orbit? Would not the moon, if it were at rest, assuredly fall to the earth, like the apple, except that, as the moon is so much larger than the apple, the earth would also measurably fall towards the moon at the same time?[1]

According to what law must the pull of the earth decrease as we go farther and farther away if it is to be just sufficient to keep the moon in its orbit? Newton deduced that it must weaken inversely as the square of the distance from the centre of the earth. This means that to compare the force at two distances we square each of these distances and then compare those squared distances, interchanging them, since the force corresponding to the larger distance is the smaller. An example is probably the way to make this clear. If one distance is 2 and the other 3 units (the units may be as large as you like, say a million miles), the squares are 4 and 9. Then the force at a distance of 3 will not, of course, be 9/4 times that at 2, but 4/9 times:

[1] Two bodies like the earth and the moon, approaching one another in consequence of a force of attraction between them, would move so as to keep the centre of gravity of the two always in the same place.

that is the meaning of the "inversely." He also supposed that the force, the mutual pull, was as the masses of the body: double the mass of the moon and you get twice the pull between earth and moon, and the same if you double the mass of the earth. Therefore, in his calculation it was not necessary to know the mass of the moon, because both the centrifugal force and what I can now boldly call the gravitational pull depend directly on this mass. If the moon were of half the mass that it is, both the centrifugal force and the gravitational pull would be halved and would still balance at the same distance.

Newton wrote in the note, made years afterwards, to which I have already referred, "I thereby compared the force requisite to keep the Moon in her orb with the force of gravity at the surface of the earth, and found them answer pretty nearly." You would have thought that this numerical agreement would have convinced Newton that he had the right answer to his problem, but it is pretty clear that he was not satisfied and put the problem aside. He was well on his way, perhaps, to his greatest triumph, the proof that the motions of the planets could be explained on the basis of a gravitational attraction acting inversely as the square of the distance, but not only did he publish nothing (as I have said he was always reluctant to publish) but he was not, it seems, content. Why?

Various explanations have been given, but I am convinced that the reason was as follows. In his calculation Newton compared the distance of the centre of the earth to the apple, about 4000 miles, with that of the centre of the earth to the moon, about 240,000 miles: squared them and compared them inversely, giving that the pull on a given mass at the moon's distance should be about 1/3600 of that on the same mass at the surface of the earth. That works out just about right for the pull required to keep the moon in her orbit. But this supposes that the earth pulls the apple as if the whole mass of the earth was gathered together at the centre of the earth. Is this right?

Newton was searching for some universal law, for the law which he afterwards laid down, that every little bit of matter attracts every other little bit of matter with a force given by multiplying their masses together and dividing by the square of the distance between them. Now consider the earth attracting the apple and suppose the earth divided up into small bits. Those near the apple will pull immensely harder than those on the other side of the earth, but there will be very much fewer of them. Will the extra number of the bits pulling at a distance just compensate for their greater distance, so that the pull of all of the bits adds up to give the same result as if all the mass of the earth were at one point at

the earth's centre? The answer is "Yes, if the inverse square law holds, but for no other law."
This is, however, a troublesome calculation—or
was in Newton's time. Newton could not prove
this in the Woolsthorpe days and I am sure that
this is what vexed him. This way of thinking of
his, the way of stating the problem and the way
of setting about solving it, was worlds away
from that of Kepler and the astronomers of his
time. It was completely in the modern spirit, an
attempt to find simple, precise mathematical
laws from which the observed measurements
could be worked out in detail. Some years afterwards Newton did prove this central attraction
and not long after published an immense ex-
tension of this early work—an immense exten-
sion, but nevertheless a development of these
great early achievements. How this came about
we shall see later.

There can be little doubt that in this Woolsthorpe period Newton had already in his head
the laws of motion which he published years
later and which are known as *Newton's laws of
motion*. The first is that a body that is at rest
will continue at rest unless a force acts on it, or
a body that is moving steadily in a straight line
will continue to move with the same speed (or
let us say velocity, the scientist's word for it) in
a straight line unless a force acts on it. As has
been already said, the ancients, and Kepler, be-

lieved that to keep a body moving at a steady speed required a force, because, in practice, a moving body stops in the end if not pushed. Newton realised that this stopping is due to friction, which is a force acting on the body. A thrown body departs from the line of the direction in which it is thrown because the force of gravity acts on it: if it is thrown horizontally, its forward velocity would continue to be the same, were it not for the resistance of the air, but its path is curved because at the same time as it moves forward it is falling, with ever-increasing velocity. This tendency to stay put or to continue moving steadily in a straight line, is, as has been said, called *inertia*. Some effects of it are familiar to everybody. If you are standing in a train which is moving at a steady velocity you, too, are, of course, moving at the same steady velocity. If the train suddenly stops, you continue moving in the straight line until the force of your impact with the carriage wall stops you. If a lift starts going down suddenly and rapidly your insides tend to stay at rest until dragged by the rest of your body: you have a queer sensation. This kind of trouble arises in aeroplanes when the speed or direction changes suddenly, but not when the aeroplane is travelling in a straight line at a fixed speed, however great. If you get out of a car that is moving you have the exact velocity with which the car was moving forward and need by bodily twists to regulate carefully the system of forces that brings you to rest.

Newton's second law of motion is to the effect that force is measured by rate of change of motion. A simple case is fall under gravity: the force is fixed and therefore the rate of change of motion, that is, the rate of change of velocity, is fixed. Thus, in falling from rest, the velocity at the end of the first second is 32.2 feet per second: at the end of the second second it is 64.4 feet per second: at the end of the third 96.6 feet per second and so on. It falls 16.1 feet in the first second: 64.4 feet in the first two seconds: and so on, multiplying 16.1 by the squares of the successive natural numbers. Of course this is a particularly simple case. If a body is attracted by a magnet, the force increases as the body nears the magnet and not only the velocity but the *rate of increase* of velocity increases.

The third law of motion is that action and reaction are equal and opposite: that is, to take an example, that the moon pulls the earth with the same force with which the earth pulls the moon. The apple also pulls the earth with the same force with which the earth pulls the apple, but whereas this little force gives the apple a visible change of motion, it does not have any measurable effect on the mass of the earth. A trick question that may make this clear is, how could you get off a sheet of perfectly smooth ice, with which your feet (or hands) had no friction at all. The answer is, take off your shoes and throw them horizontally: your shoes, as they leave your hand, will push you with the same force with which you push your shoes, and if you weigh 100 times as much as your shoes you will move with 1/100th of the speed with which they leave you. As there is no friction, you will, by the first law, travel steadily at this rate until you reach the edge of the ice, where there is friction to stop you.

When, more than twenty years later, he published his great book the *Principia,* of which we talk in Chapter V, Newton gave precise expression to these laws. We have no record of them in the Woolsthorpe period, but from what he did, he must have known them.

At Woolsthorpe Newton made great discoveries which founded the supremely important branch of mathematics known as the differential and integral calculus. A few words are necessary to explain what is meant by these terms. Ordinary algebra, as taught in schools, deals with certain unknown quantities, represented by letters, which, under given conditions, have certain values: quite often the problem is to find the particular numerical value which agrees with the circumstances set down in the question. However, in many fields of mathematics we are faced with two quantities which vary continuously, the one with the other, and we are interested in rates of variation. Consider any curve, say an oval or a parabola. At any particular point there can be drawn a line touching it, the so-called tangent. If you are not a mathematician, think of a smoothly curved hill: the tangent will correspond to the steepness at any point and will be given by the rate at which the height varies with the horizontal distance. If when you advance one yard horizontally the height increases by 1 foot, then the steepness, or slope of the tangent, is 1/3rd: the next advance of one yard horizontally may increase the height by only 99/100 of a foot, in which case the slope will diminish by one hundredth. But clearly if the hill is really perfectly smoothly curved and you are measuring with mathematical accuracy, the slope will vary with every inch, or fraction of an inch, advanced, and to find the slope *absolutely accurately* at each point you must consider what the change of height divided by the change of horizontal distance becomes when they are both very small indeed. You are concerned with the rate at which height varies with horizontal advance. For certain problems you may be concerned with the rate at which the *slope* varies as you advance. For instance, suppose that there is a little flat place on the hillside, where the slope becomes nothing and then increases again.

Mathematically this means that, for a moment, the slope does not change as you advance, or the rate of change with advance, of the rate of change of height with advance, is nothing: we are dealing with a rate of change of a rate of change—a second rate of change, as it is called. Perhaps I have said enough to convince you that in dealing with curves—or solids—the mathematician is concerned with the rate at which one quantity varies with another.

Or think of problems of velocity. Here the distance from a point varies with time: we are concerned with a rate of change of distance with time. Thus, give a ball a push so that it rolls on a flat floor: it goes slower and slower until it stops. The rate of change of its distance from the starting point diminishes gradually to zero. We have seen that force is measured by rate of change of velocity, that is, by second rate of change of distance from a point. In this case the force in question is the force of friction, which may vary from point to point of the floor. You can see at once how important the mathematics of rates of change and of second rates of change, must be for mechanics.

We can have further rates: in problems of the bending of flat horizontal beams we are faced with the rate of change, of the rate of change, of the rate of change, of the rate of change of the droop with distance from one end.

One problem, then, is, given a relation between one quantity and another, to find the rate of change or the second rate of change. This is the simplest kind of problem of the differential calculus. You may, however, have the reverse problem: you may be given information about rates—or second rates—of change, and have to find, backwards, how the one quantity varies with the other. This is the simplest kind of problem of the integral calculus. Take an elementary problem: when a body falls freely, the acceleration, that is, the rate of change of velocity or second rate of change of distance from the starting point, is known: it is the so-called gravitational acceleration. Find how the distance from the starting point increases with the time. If we are considering smooth curves, the differential calculus is concerned with the slope of the tangent and the integral calculus with the area enclosed,[2] in the simplest case.

All this can be summed up by saying that the calculus is a branch of mathematics concerned with rates of variation. In physical and astronomical problems we are nearly always dealing with rates.

Before leaving Cambridge for Woolsthorpe Newton had made an important mathematical discovery connected with series, but, he writes

[2] If the curve is not closed, then the area enclosed by it and certain straight lines.

himself, "About that time the Plague breaking out, obliged me to go hence from Cambridge and think of something else." This discovery enabled him to calculate the area of the curve called the hyperbola and he adds, "I am ashamed to tell to how many places of figures I carried these computations, having no other business at the time." This numerical calculation for calculation's sake is akin to Newton's fondness for copying drawings and such like, a way, as he suggests, of amusing himself in his spare time. When he was at Woolsthorpe he followed up his work on series and busied himself with what he called "fluxions," that is, flowing quantities or, speaking in the language of to-day, rates of change. In short, he discovered the principles of the differential and integral calculus. Some of the greatest of his predecessors were feeling their way towards them, but it was Newton who plainly grasped the principles concerned.

In 1716 he wrote, "I invented the method of series and fluxions in the year 1665, improved them in the year 1666, and I still have in my custody several mathematical papers written in the years 1664, 1665, 1666, some of which happen to be dated." He did not at the time publish his results or tell anybody what he was doing, and it was not till 1669, when, remember, Newton was still only twenty-six, that he gave Barrow a written account of some of his work, which was handed round among a few prominent mathematicians, but not published until over thirty years later. This shrinking from publication caused a great deal of trouble, for the German mathematician Leibniz (sometimes spelt Leibnitz) also discovered the method of the calculus, and published his results, which gave rise to long and unfortunate disputes as to who was first, since some said that Leibniz had come to hear of Newton's work. Probably the discoveries were independent. The eminent mathematician H. W. Turnbull, writing of these disputes, says, "Had Newton set out to record his mathematics with the open-handed liberality of a Wallis,[3] who delighted in revealing not only the finished results but all his tricks and methods, and who taught as he wrote, how different would have been the sequel. . . . After reading Wallis, Barrow and Gregory, to read the *De Analysi* of Newton [the mathematical paper, in Latin, which Newton gave to Barrow in 1669] is to enter a new world. The power, directness and sureness of touch compel attention: and these features shine through all his work." So much, at the moment, for the mathematics of our young man in his early twenties.

The other great problem in which Newton

[3] James Wallis and James Gregory were outstanding mathematicians who lived in the time of Newton.

made fundamental advances at Woolsthorpe was that of the composition of white light. In his first published paper, some years later, he says, ". . . in the beginning of the year 1666 (at which time I applied myself to the grinding of optic glasses of other figures than spherical) I procured a triangular prism to try therewith the celebrated phenomena of colours" and then proceeds to describe his experiments. Which of them were done at Woolsthorpe and which at Cambridge, however, it is not possible to say, but from the date some of them must have been carried out at Woolsthorpe, and I have little doubt that he was well on the way to his chief results before he left. We will, however, talk about these results when we come to the publication of his paper, which was an important event, as we shall see.

In the eighteen months or so at Woolsthorpe, then, the young Newton mastered the basic laws of mechanics; convinced himself that they applied to heavenly as well as to earthly bodies and discovered the fundamental law of gravitational attraction: invented the methods of the infinitesimal calculus: and was well on the way to his great optical discoveries. What he did later went, of course, immensely further, but it all grew out of the results won in that wonderful period, it was all built on the foundations then laid. ". . . For in those days I was in the prime of my age for invention, and minded mathematics and philosophy more than at any time since." We can well believe it.

IV

Newton Comes Before the World

It was early in 1667 that Newton returned to Cambridge and he was soon elected what was then called a Minor Fellow of Trinity College. Next year he became a Major Fellow, which gave him a good position and showed that he was then recognised in the College as a man much above the average, very likely as a result of Barrow's belief in him. There were, about this time, several vacancies among the Fellows: two of them had fallen downstairs, with serious results, no doubt after a long sitting with the bottle, and another, a Senior Fellow, had been put out of the College on account of insanity. The year after the award of the Senior Fellowship, Isaac Barrow resigned his position and arranged for Newton, now twenty-six years old, to succeed him as Lucasian Professor of Mathematics. In the book on optics which he published in the year of his retirement from the Professorship he acknowledges Newton's help in the preface, calling him (in Latin, of course: it was the custom for learned men to publish their books in this language, so that they could be read by the learned all over Europe) "a man of quite exceptional ability and singular skill," which he certainly was!

About this time Newton was keenly interested in his work on optics. He had not lost his interest in handicraft: he ground and polished his own lenses and it seems that he made with his own hands the machines for doing this. Of course in those days you could not buy the particular lenses you wanted in Cambridge, or elsewhere, so that it was a great advantage to make your own, and, further, Newton tried, without much success, to make lenses with surfaces of special non-spherical shapes, which offers the greatest difficulty, even to-day. He seems to have been the first man to use pitch for optical polishing, as they do now and was, evidently, a first-rate man at the job. "If I had stayed for other people to make my tools and things for me I had never made anything of it," he said later.

I have already referred to his work with the prism. His chief experiments were on the following lines. He worked in a dark room, into which a small beam of bright sunlight came through a round hole. Arranging a prism in the beam, he found that the white light was spread out into a coloured strip, in which the colours were, in succession, red, orange, yellow, green, blue, indigo, violet (Fig. 3). Such a strip of coloured lights is called a spectrum. He must have had a very

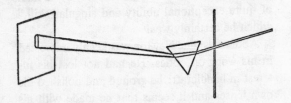

Fig. 3. The arrangement of Newton's simplest experiment with the prism, copied from his book 'Opticks' (see Chapter VI)

keen sense of colour: some people with quite a good sense of colour do not see indigo as a really distinct colour between blue and violet. He found that the appearance could be explained if light of different colours was differently bent in passing through the prism, the red least and the violet most, and the other colours in between. Then if all the colours were present together in the original white light they would be separated out after passing through the prism. He proved his belief that the different colours all mixed together make white light by bringing them all together so as to overlap: he found that they produced light "entirely and perfectly white."

The really decisive experiment was called by Newton, when he published later, the *experimentum crucis,* the supreme test. He let the beam of white light fall on a prism and be spread out into a spectrum. With a board with a hole in it he cut off all light but one colour, say the red, and let the red beam so separated pass through a second prism. It was bent by the same amount as in the first prism and remained exactly the same red. If the blue beam was let through, and fell on the second prism, it was more bent than the red beams, and remained the same blue (Fig. 4). In this kind of way he

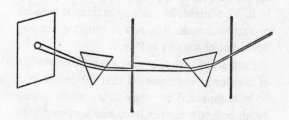

*Fig. 4. The crucial experiment, copied, with
slight simplification, from the 'Opticks'*

demonstrated clearly that to each colour corresponds a certain bending aside when the light passes from air to glass. The amount of bending depends, of course, on the angle at which the beam strikes the glass surface, but for a given angle it is always greater for blue light than for red. There is a number, called the refractive index, that measures the bendability—the refrangibility, as Newton called it—of each kind of light. In Newton's own words, "And so the true cause of the length of the image [the spectrum] was detected to be no other, than that light consists of rays differently refrangible, which were, according to their degrees of refrangibility, transmitted towards divers parts of the wall." That is the heart of the matter, put with Newton's usual clearness. He insisted that the coloured lights were there already in the white beam: once a coloured beam, say blue, had been separated out, it stayed blue whatever you did to it. You might, he said, by making it broader or narrower make it fainter or brighter, but you could not change its colour.

Connected with this was another observation of Newton's. He observed that the image of a body illuminated by white light, when formed by an ordinary convex lens, was bordered with colour. You can easily check this by forming an image of the sun with a simple lens on a piece of white paper. You may also like to repeat a simple experiment which Newton did. He painted an oblong strip of card one-half pure red and the other half pure blue, and wound a fine thread of very black silk round and round so as to form black lines on the red and blue background. He then brightly illuminated the paper—he used a candle but you can do much better with an electric lamp—and, with a simple convex lens, focused the black threads on to a piece of white paper. When those on the red paper were sharp those on the blue were out of focus and blurred: when the blue were sharp, those on the red were out of focus and blurred. If the red were sharp he had to move the white paper nearer to the lens to get the blue sharp. The lens, of course, forms the image by bending the light: these results can be explained at once on the ground that blue light is bent more than red.

From these experiments Newton came to the conclusion that with lenses, however you shaped them, you could never make a telescope that would give a good image, free from colour fringes. He was absolutely right if you use only one kind of glass. What he did not know is that different kinds of glass separate out red and blue by different amounts: the result of this is that, by combining lenses made of different, suitably chosen, glasses, you can get rid of coloured edges to a great extent. Lenses free from bad colour effects are called achromatic, but they came much later. It was John Dollond who discovered how to make them and he, ably supported and followed by his son Peter Dollond, put the English telescope in front of all others for a long time.

There is, however, a way of forming an image of a bright object without lenses, and that is by using a concave mirror. With a mirror, light of all colours is reflected at the same angle, so that we are not troubled with coloured edges when we are concerned with white light. The construction of a reflecting telescope had been proposed by James Gregory, the distinguished Scottish mathematician and astronomer, a few years before, in 1663, but he had not made one and he did not realise its great advantage, namely getting rid of colour effects. Newton set to work to construct a reflecting telescope with his own hands. The mirror was made of metal; he used a special alloy which he prepared himself, of copper, tin and arsenic, called speculum metal, speculum being Latin for a mirror. It is white, like silver, and takes a particularly good polish. He ground the mirror into a hollow, like a saucer—but, of course, part of a perfect sphere —and polished it: it was quite small, little more than an inch across. He arranged it, as in the diagram (Fig. 5), so that the rays thrown back were reflected out sideways by a small flat metal mirror. Later Newton used a right-angled prism for this reflexion, as shown in the diagram; he was the first to use this device. The image formed by the concave mirror he magnified with

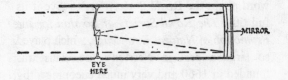

Fig. 5. The principles of the construction of Newton's reflecting telescope from the 'Opticks'

a lens inserted on the side of the tube. In a letter dated February 23, 1688, he says that the instrument was only six inches long, but magnified forty times, and he says at the end of the letter, "This [that is, the superiority of the reflecting telescope over a telescope made with lenses] is the necessary consequence of some experiments, which I have made concerning the nature of light." We know now what he meant, but I doubt if the man who received the letter did. It is worth remembering that the largest telescopes of modern times, the 100-inch[1] at Mount Wilson and the 200-inch at Mount Palomar are reflecting, or mirror, telescopes. The mirrors are made of glass, coated on the front with a very thin layer of bright metal, which does the reflecting, so that, in a way, they are metallic reflectors.

[1] This means that the mirror is 100 inches across.

We must interrupt our story here to say a word about the Royal Society, or, to give it its full title, *The Royal Society of London for the Promotion of Natural Knowledge,* which played so large a part in Newton's life. This was founded in 1660 and very much encouraged by King Charles II who gave it two years later, what is called its Charter, a document establishing its rights and privileges. It is still the premier scientific society in the world. It took as its motto *Nullius in verba,* part of a Latin quotation which may be freely translated as, "We don't take anybody's word for it." At that time, as has been said earlier, it was a common thing, if you wanted to know some particular of the nature of motion or of light, for instance, to find out what Aristotle, or some other great Greek philosopher, had written on the point and to suppose and say that that settled the matter. The men who founded the Royal Society, however, believed in experiment, believed that the way to find out how things happened was to observe and the way to find out if your notions were right was to see what conclusions they led you to and then to put those conclusions to the test. You may think, to-day, that everybody would have agreed that this was the sensible way of going about things, but this was not so. Many people attacked the Society and its principles, saying, in effect, "So you think that you know better than Aristotle, who was worth all of you put together" or "So you think you know better than Descartes, whom every educated man recognises as the greatest thinker of modern times." The attitude of the Royal Society is reflected in something that Newton himself said when, towards the end of his life a friend told him of some astronomical observations which were thought—wrongly—to be against the Newtonian system. He replied, "It may be so, there is no arguing against facts and experiments."

When Newton made his first reflecting telescope it aroused great interest at Cambridge and news of it came to the Royal Society in London, which expressed an urgent wish to see it. In response, Newton made a second and better one, which he sent: it is to-day one of the most treasured possessions of the Society. The mirror is about two inches across and the telescope nine inches long. The instrument was received with enthusiasm: Newton was elected a Fellow of the Royal Society and he was asked for a written account of the invention. In reply he wrote:

"At the reading of your letter I was surprised to see so much care taken about securing an invention to me, of which I have hitherto had so little value. And therefore since the Royal Society is pleased to think it worth the patronising, I must acknowledge it deserves much more of them for that, than of me, who, had not the communication of it been desired, might have let it remain in private as it hath already done some years."

Here we see clearly set down how little he cared for public acknowledgment or fame. This might be supposed to be mock modesty by those who have not studied Newton, but it is quite clear that the only reason that he sent the telescope was that it was urgently asked for. The result of this keen interest, however, was that Newton now offered to send an account of the "philosophical discovery," as he called it, that led him to make the instrument, which, he suggested, was much more interesting than the instrument. In due course he sent this account and it was published in the Transactions of the Royal Society early in 1672—the first printed account of any of Newton's discoveries.

In this paper Newton gives an account of the experiments with the prism, and of the conclusions from them, which I have already described. He starts by saying that it was at the beginning of 1666 that he carried out the first experiments. The paper met with much applause and it was at once realised that here was something of the highest importance: the Society appointed a committee to judge of its value. Robert Hooke was a member of this committee and wrote the report, which speaks very highly of the experiments but brings certain criticisms about their interpretation, based on an ingenious theory of light which Hooke himself had put forward. Hooke was an older man than Newton, a man of immense ingenuity and scientific perception and an experimenter of the first rank. He was also of a very irritable nature and often thought, sometimes with full justice, that due credit had not been given to him for his discoveries. Newton, also an irritable man, took his criticisms on this occasion well, but later there was much dispute between the two men, which was deliberately fostered by Oldenburg, then secretary of the Royal Society, and an enemy of Hooke's. Huygens also criticised Newton's work: he was committed to the lens telescope and that may have influenced his judgment. What he failed to understand was that Newton was not arguing about the nature of colour, about matters of doctrine, but describing experiments to show how white light and coloured light behaved, to show what were the measurable properties. You will bear with me if I quote Newton's words again: in spite of a somewhat old-fashioned turn of phrase they express the point so well and show so clearly his masterly mind. He wrote, ". . . the Theory, which I propounded, was evinced by me, not by inferring 'tis thus because not otherwise, that is, not by deducing it only from a confutation of contrary suppositions, but by deriving it from Experiments concluding positively and directly." Another critic was the Frenchman, Father Ignatius Pardies: he was very courteous and in the end apologised for having misunderstood Newton, who was courteous in return and once more expressed his point of view, "For the best and safest method of philosophising [doing scientific work] we should say seems to be, first to inquire diligently into the properties of things, and of establishing these properties by experiment, and then to proceed more slowly to hypotheses [theories] for the explanation of them." So this incident passed off. Another critic, however, a Belgian named Linus, who was a stupid, ignorant and narrow-minded man, printed some absurd and not very polite criticisms of the work, which Newton at first refused to answer, but Linus persisted, and was followed by another quarrelsome nobody. I mention all this because it had a most unfortunate effect on Newton, who hated dispute of this kind, and wrote in 1676, "I see I have made myself a slave to philosophy, but if I get free of Mr. Linus's business I will resolutely bid adieu to it eternally, excepting what I do for my private satisfaction, or leave to come out after me; for I see a man must either resolve to put out nothing new, or become a slave to defend it"—my discoveries, he was saying in effect, shall either not be published at all, or after my death. This is characteristic and does much to explain Newton's aversion to publication. His work was so new that it was bound to be misunderstood by even clever men, let alone people like Linus, but Newton regarded such misunderstanding as a kind of deliberate persecution which he would not stand. What made things worse was that Oldenburg was always nagging him to answer criticisms that he wished to ignore.

Before the letter from which I have just quoted Newton had sent a second paper about light to the Royal Society, in which he put forward a theory to explain the experiments on the prism and also the brilliant colours shown by thin sheets, such as flakes of mica and the walls of soap bubbles. This again led to trouble with Hooke, who had already published an account of experiments on these colours of thin plates. Newton's theory was a most remarkable feat, which is difficult to explain simply without a long discussion of many hard points. In most books it is stated that Newton considered a beam of light to be a stream of little particles and so the term "corpuscular theory" is used, since a corpuscle means a very small particle. However, Newton, to explain some of the experiments, and particularly the colours of thin plates, was led to give to light not only particle properties, but also wave properties. In the past century and the very early years of the present century all men of science believed light to consist of waves of a particular kind, but now it is held that light has some particle properties and some wave properties, which is just the conclusion Newton reached. His theory was, of course, a long way from the present theory, but where the facts known to him needed waves to explain them, on modern views, is just where he decided on wave properties.

Here we have Newton, then, in the early thirties of his age, known to the scientific world, which practically means Western Europe, as a brilliant investigator, but exasperated at the criticism that the publication of his researches had aroused. He fell into a distaste for science. When Hooke, who had become secretary of the Royal Society and was, at the time, on moderately good terms with him, wrote very civilly asking him for a paper for the Society, Newton replied that his interest in 'philosophy' was worn out and that he preferred to spend his time on something else. In his letter, however, Hooke asked Newton what he thought of a supposition that he, Hooke, had printed at the end of a paper in 1674. In this Hooke had actually suggested that the planets would move steadily in straight lines in the absence of any force and that what kept a planet in its orbit was a central force drawing it aside, this force decreasing with increase of the distance. In his letter of reply Newton did not answer the question, but, referring to something else, made a slip which Hooke somewhat tactlessly corrected and so once more offended Newton. In a further letter Hooke actually suggested the inverse square law of force. Newton, we know, had already concluded years ago that this was the correct law, but Hooke did not, and could not, know of this. There is little doubt that this correspondence revived Newton's interest in the problem of the planetary movements, in spite of his words of indifference. We see, too, the seeds of fresh trouble between the two great scientists.

This question of the planetary motions was occupying the minds of many prominent Fellows of the Royal Society about this time. Early in 1684, the great astronomer Edmond Halley, whose name is known to most people from "Halley's comet," met with Sir Christopher Wren and Robert Hooke—probably in a coffee-house—to talk about the matter. Hooke affirmed that the laws of the celestial motions followed from the inverse square law and that he had proved this. Sir Christopher, who was evidently a bit doubtful, said that he would give Hooke two months' time to produce the proof and would present him with a book costing 40 shil-

lings if he did it. Hooke put him off: I believe
that Hooke was convinced that the inverse
square law was at the bottom of the matter, and
had some kind of general indication and argu-
ments, but no mathematical proof. He was not
an outstanding mathematician: in any case he
did not produce what was required. In the following August Halley went to Cambridge to get
Newton's views. He asked him what would be
the orbit described by a planet supposing that it
was attracted to the sun by a gravitational force
obeying an inverse square law. Newton immediately answered *an ellipse*. "Struck with joy and
amazement" to quote the record of the meeting,
"Halley asked him how he knew it. Why, replied he, I have calculated it; and being asked
for the calculation, he could not find it, but
promised to send it to him." It is typical of Newton not to be able to lay hands on a little thing
like that: he was not concerned about it at the
time. Soon after he sent Halley two different
proofs of the elliptic orbit, and, his interest having been revived by this, he wrote down the
principles of mechanics in a little book *De
Motu Corporum* (On the Movements of Bodies) which was founded on his lectures. This he
sent to Halley at the end of the year. Halley at
once saw the overwhelming importance of Newton's work and made up his mind to induce

Newton to write a treatise setting out in detail his discoveries.

The stage was now set for the appearance of what is held by most men of science to be the greatest scientific book ever written, Newton's *Principia*.

V

The Principia

HALLEY, then, who was not only a great astronomer but a man with a keen sense of what was really important and a man of great energy—and also of tact, which does not always go with energy—had made up his mind that Newton's discoveries must be published without delay, and set about persuading Newton to write a book describing them. In this he had the sanction and support of the Royal Society, now also convinced that something extraordinary was in question. In the end Newton agreed and in 1685 he set about the task. It was in April 1686 that the manuscript of the first book was sent to the Royal Society, for the work was divided into three sections which Newton called 'Books,' although they were all to be bound in one volume. It is recorded in the Minutes of the Royal Society for April 28th that "Dr. Vincent presented to the Society a manuscript treatise entitled *Philosophiae Naturalis Principia Mathematica,* and dedicated to the Society by Mr. Isaac Newton, wherein he gives a mathematical demonstration of the Copernican hypothesis as proposed by Kepler, and makes out all the phenomena of the celestial motions by the only supposition of a gravitation towards the centre of the sun decreasing as the squares of the distances therefrom reciprocally," which is quite a good description of the first book. The second and third books followed later. The whole work, which was written in Latin, the language of the learned world, had taken about eighteen months to complete; a prodigious feat. While the full title is *Philosophiae Naturalis Principia Mathematica,* The Mathematical Principles of Natural Philosophy, it is always referred to as the *Principia.*

The history of the production of the book was not a smooth one and it is entirely due to Halley that it appeared in its final form. From what has already been said about Newton's character it will be understood that, to begin with, it was difficult enough to bring him to the point of agreeing to write the book. To save Newton trouble, Halley undertook to see the book through the press, as the saying is, that is, to arrange with the printer about the style of printing, to assist in the preparation of the diagrams, to help in correcting the proofs and, in general, to be responsible for the many questions of detail which, I can assure the reader, arise in the production of a book, especially a big scientific book with mathematics and diagrams. The Royal Society was not well off, so Halley undertook to bear the expense of printing. Then trouble with Hooke started. He suddenly learnt that, six years after his courteous letter about the inverse square law, Newton was going to publish the solution of the problem of the planetary motions, based on the lines which he had suggested. All that he wanted, apparently, was some kind of acknowledgment: in a letter to Newton Halley wrote, "Only Mr. Hooke seems to expect you should make some mention of him in the preface, which it is possible you may see reason to prefix." This was not unreasonable. Hooke did not know, as we do, that, long before his letter, Newton had arrived at the inverse square law from his considerations of the moon's motion. We may admit that Hooke could not furnish a proper mathematical solution of the problem, but even to us it appears quite possible that it was his letter that led Newton to start working again on the planetary orbits.

A generous word in the preface would have cost Newton nothing. However, probably with the former disputes in mind, he at once took offence. He wrote a very angry letter to Halley in which he said that he would suppress the third book, which treated of the system of the world and was the crown of the work. He declared "Philosophy [Science] is such an impertinently litigious Lady, that a man had as good be engaged in lawsuits, as have to do with her. I found it so formerly, and now I am no sooner come near her again, but she gives me warning." So the earlier criticisms were still rankling. He bitterly attacked Hooke in the same letter, and wrote about "this new provocation." Halley succeeded in calming him down and persuaded him not to suppress the third book. Evidently, as usual, someone had been making mischief, for Halley wrote, "As to the manner of Mr. Hooke's claiming this discovery, I fear it has been represented in worse colours than it ought: for he neither made public application to the Society for justice, nor pretended you had all from him," and goes on to say that what Hooke claimed at the coffee-house was "that he gave you the first hint of this invention." In his reply Newton agrees that Hooke had been misrepresented to him and expresses regret for some of the things he had written. Finally, he did insert a short note in the *Principia* where he first mentions the inverse square law, saying that Sir Christopher Wren,

Dr. Hooke and Dr. Halley had already put it forward.

As for Newton's life at the time when he was writing the book, we have some notes made, years after, by Humphrey Newton—no relation —who acted as his secretary from 1685 to 1690 and who actually made the fair copy of the manuscript from which the book was printed. This fair copy is now in the possession of the Royal Society. He tells us that Newton very seldom went to bed until two or three in the morning, and sometimes not until five or six and that he lay in bed only four or five hours. On the other hand Newton himself, in his old age, told his friend Stukeley, who wrote it down, that even when he was working hardest he never forgot to go to bed about midnight. It may be that Humphrey Newton remembered very well being kept up late on a few occasions when he wanted to go to bed and that Isaac Newton only remembered his rule and forgot that he sometimes broke it.

There are many stories, from people who knew him, concerning his absent-mindedness about this time. Stukeley tells us that when he had friends in his rooms, if he went into his study for a bottle of wine and a thought came into his head, he would sit down to write and forget his friends. Humphrey Newton says that he often forgot to eat, unless reminded and also that "He kept neither dog nor cat in his chamber, which made well for the old woman his bedmaker, she faring much the better for it, for in a morning she has sometimes found both dinner and supper scarcely tasted of, which the old woman has very pleasantly and mumpingly gone away with." If he was walking in his garden at Trinity College he would suddenly halt, turn round and then run upstairs to write, standing at a desk, what had come into his head, in too much of a hurry to draw up a chair. He was only ill once in the five years that Humphrey Newton was with him, and then appeared not to care if he lived or died. When Humphrey seemed very concerned at his illness Newton told him not to trouble himself, for if he died he was leaving him a legacy. He was not a very emotional man.

At the time that he was writing the *Principia* he was also carrying out chemical experiments, about which I shall say a word later. Newton used, for heating his materials in the laboratory, brick-built furnaces, which he constructed with his own hands. These few incidents may give some notion of the life of this extraordinary man while writing the *Principia:* full of his thoughts, which were written down, either in stretches or suddenly as they came into his head, with meals and company forgotten; concentrated on chemical experiments when he was not writing, or thinking about, his book; disturbed by no emotions; arousing wonder, astonishment and a kind of admiration in his assistant, but, apparently, no affection.

In July 1686 Samuel Pepys was President of the Royal Society. He was a man almost without scientific knowledge of any kind, but very shrewd, influential, well-liked and interested in the doings of learned men, whom he admired. In that month he put his name to the imprimatur of the *Principia,* in token that the Royal Society sanctioned and approved the book. It seems strange, but there, on the title page, stands the name of Pepys just as prominently displayed as that of Newton. The manuscript then went to the printer and the book duly appeared next year, that is, round about midsummer, 1687. Halley wrote to Newton sending him twenty free copies and forty more for the Cambridge booksellers, with instructions as to what price they were to have them for, since Halley, you will remember, had financed the book and naturally hoped to get some of his money back. It was all very business-like: unbound they were to be 6 shillings "to take my money as they are sold" or 5 shillings for ready money, "for," he writes, "I am satisfied that there is no dealing in books without interesting the booksellers, and I am contented to let them go halves with me." Copies of the book are worth considerably more now!

The *Principia* was not an easy book to read then, neither is it now. The mathematical methods which Newton uses are those of classical geometry, which could then be followed by good mathematicians only and with which few are really familiar to-day. It is generally much simpler to obtain the results by using the calculus which Newton had invented, but in this book these methods were not used. Many think that he employed the calculus to reach his conclusions and then provided geometrical proofs, because he greatly admired the mathematical methods of the ancients. In any case he told a friend that, "to avoid being bated by little smatterers in mathematics he designedly made his *Principia* abstruse; but yet so as to be understood by able mathematicians." We see again his horror of being annoyed by people who could not understand him, and his feeling of persecution. If duller men queried anything in his work he considered that they were "baiting" him. He also says in the book that many of his propositions would need a long time to master, even by good mathematicians, and indicates to the reader what he can skip and still understand the third book, where the system of the world is worked out.

Let us briefly consider what this extraordinary work contains. It starts with a clear statement of the laws of motion to which I have already referred. In the course of the discussion due acknowledgment is made to Galileo's services. Newton proceeds very cautiously and refuses to discuss causes which cannot be checked by experiment and observation. He writes, for example, in this first book—translated here, of course, from the Latin—"For I here design only to give mathematical notion of those forces, without considering their physical causes and seats," and a little later he says, "Wherefore the reader is not to imagine that by those words I anywhere take upon me to define the kind, or the manner of any action, the causes or the physical reasons thereof, or that I attribute forces, in a true and physical sense, to certain centres (which are only mathematical points), when at any time I happen to speak of centres as attracting, or as endowed with attractive powers." He insists, in effect, that, if you allow that mathematical points have mass and attract one another, and behave in general according to his laws, then he will show you how to work out results which agree closely with what can be observed, and which enable you to foretell what can be expected to happen, but he does not intend to discuss the reason or the final cause of the forces in question. In the same way, in a letter written six years later he says to Richard

Bentley, the great scholar and critic, "You sometimes speak of gravity as essential and inherent to matter. Pray do not ascribe that notion to me; for the cause of gravity is what I do not pretend to know. . . ." People sometimes ask, "What is electricity?" and say that nobody knows. What kind of an answer they expect or have in mind it is hard to guess. Probably if Newton had written on electricity and had been asked this question he would have replied that he did not pretend to know, that he was concerned with how electricity behaved, with the mathematical laws from which you could deduce the measured electrical forces and effects. This attitude of Newton's is that of modern science, but it was new in his time and was one of the things that people trained in the old philosophy found hard to understand.

After the discussion of the laws of mechanics and the inverse square law Newton proceeds to prove Kepler's laws of planetary motion and further, the important point which I have already mentioned, that an attracting sphere behaves as if the mass were all concentrated at the centre. After this he works out fully the problem of two bodies attracting one another, such as the earth and the moon. Newton laid down that every particle of matter gravitationally attracted every other particle of matter according to the inverse square law: therefore every planet

attracts any other planet and the sun, as well as
the earth, attracts the moon. The reason that the
orbits of the planets are almost exactly ellipses
is that the sun is so massive compared to the
planets and the planets are so far apart. Actually the sun contains about a third of a million
times as much matter as the earth and getting
on for a thousand times as much matter as all
the planets together, so that it is really the master and, in considering the motion of a particular planet, we can base our calculations on the
attraction between it and the sun, and need not,
until it comes to very great precision, pay attention to the very small attractions of the other
planets.

The moon is so close to the earth, compared
to its distance from the sun, that the attraction
of the earth is the chief control, but the sun's
attraction on both earth and moon has to be
taken into account and is responsible for many
irregularities in the moon's motion which have
been known for centuries. Newton considers
the effect of a third attracting body, but this is
an extraordinarily complicated question which
has occupied many great mathematicians ever
since his time and he could only make a start
on it. Still, make a good start he did. He developed the laws of pendulum motion, with due
acknowledgments to Huygens, who had already
done much in that line. This first book of the

Principia is a great treatise on mechanics, written in the modern spirit if not worked out by modern methods, and nearly everything in it was a pioneering new discovery.

In the first book all the motions are considered as taking place in empty space, with no resistance offered to the movement. In the second book Newton deals with motions in surroundings that offer resistance, such as, say, bodies moving in or on water. In some of his problems he foreshadows the kind of resistance offered by the air to aeroplanes. One question which he tackles is that of the shape that will meet with least resistance, which he says, "may be of use in the building of ships." He does not give details as to how he reaches his results on this particular subject, but from them, and a calculation which he did later, it is clear that he must have discovered the principles of a branch of mathematics known as the calculus of variations, a little matter of which he nowhere leaves any record. He also deals with the motion of pendulums when there is air resistance. Perhaps the most important among the many astonishing things in this book is the mathematical treatment of wave motion; certain fundamental results are here given for the first time. Everybody knows the great part which waves play in modern science. Here again it was Newton who first showed the way.

You will remember Descartes' notion that the heavenly bodies were dragged round by a great whirlpool of minute particles. Let us examine this mathematically, says Newton in effect. In order to drag a body, a fluid must offer resistance to its motion, for if the body could slip through without resistance it would stay put and the fluid just move past it. Very well, then, what would be the laws of motion of a body carried round by a vortex of a fluid of the required kind? He shows that they would be nothing like Kepler's laws: in particular, the year would vary with the radius of the orbit in a way very different from that actually measured. There are other difficulties, such as the source of the energy which the moving body uses up. In this way, by precise calculation, Newton disposes of the vortices of Descartes. He shows a certain satisfaction in having cleared up this matter, a satisfaction which is unusual for him to display.

The third book is a triumph. After giving a summary of what has been done in the first two books he announces that from the same principles he will now demonstrate the structure of the system of the world—and proceeds to do so, with such thoroughness that what was done in the next two hundred years, by some of the most able minds in science, was largely extensions and improvements of his work. He runs through the motions of the satellites of Jupiter and Sat-

urn and the Earth, and of the planets round the
sun in terms of his gravitational theory, in part
reconsidering and extending the results of Book
I. He then breaks completely new ground. He
shows how to find the masses of the sun and of
the planets from the mass of the earth, for which
he gets a value quite close to that which is found
by the latest methods—that is, he says that the
density of the earth is between five and six times
that of water, and the accepted figure to-day is
almost exactly 5½. Further, the earth is flat-
tened at the poles, as are other planets. Newton
shows how to account for this mathematically
and works out a shape which agrees pretty well
with the latest measurements.

Then he proceeds to a truly astonishing feat.
It is a familiar fact that the axis of the earth is
tilted so as to make an angle of about 66½ degrees with the plane in which its orbit lies and
that it always keeps parallel to itself as it goes
round in its orbit, which accounts for summer
and winter. Actually, however, the earth's axis
does not keep *precisely* parallel to itself, but
very slowly changes its angle so as to trace out
a cone in the heavens, a movement which is
called "the precession of the equinoxes." I say
"very slowly" because it takes nearly 26,000
years to complete the cone: I need hardly add
that astronomical observations have not been
going on for long enough to measure more than

a small part of the complete cycle of once round. If the earth were a perfect sphere the Newtonian principles show that the force of the sun's attraction would pass exactly through the centre and then the axis should always stay *exactly* parallel to itself. But the earth is not a perfect sphere: it bulges slightly at the equator, and the pull of the sun on the part of the bulge near it is slightly greater than that on the part of the bulge away from it and so produces a slight force of twist. Newton worked all this out, and proved that the gravitational pull on the bulge would produce exactly the very slow movement of the direction of the axis that had been observed through the centuries. A calculation of this kind is not quite the same kind of thing as suggesting that an apple falls because the earth pulls it!

This is, however, far from all. Using results of the first book, he worked out the main irregularities of the moon's motion which were produced by the pull of the sun, and treated other satellites in the same way. He explained that the tides of the sea are due to the pull of the moon and the sun on the waters and worked out the general features of the movements, thus laying the foundation of all sound work on the theory of the tides. He turns to the comets and shows that they are members of the solar system moving under the influence of the sun's attraction and that consequently their orbits can be calculated. A single sentence summarising all this part of the work occurs in some passages which Newton added to the second edition of the *Principia*. After refusing to speculate on the cause of the power of gravity, he says, "It is enough that gravity does really exist, and act according to the laws which we have explained, and abundantly serves to account for all the motions of the celestial bodies, and of our sea."

It ought, perhaps, to be added that the *Principia* contains, besides all this marvellous theoretical and mathematical work, accounts of certain practical work, particularly some carried out with pendulums, which show that Newton was a master of experimental method. This work possibly impresses men who have themselves carried out experimental research more than it does the inexperienced: it shows such an appreciation of what does matter and what does not matter.

The book deals with many difficult matters and it is clearly not possible to explain all its excellencies in a short general account of this kind. I hope, however, that enough has been said to make it easy for the reader to understand why the *Principia* has been considered by the great men of science who came after Newton to be one of the most prodigious feats of human intellect. In fact, Laplace, the celebrated French mathematician and astronomer, wrote, "The *Principia* is pre-eminent above any other production of human genius."

The book sold readily and brought Newton great fame. A review in the French scientific periodical *Journal des Scavans* (Journal of the Learned) begins—I translate from the French— "The work of Mr. Newton is the most perfect treatise on mechanics that can be imagined, it not being possible to provide more precise or more exact demonstrations than those which he gives in the first two books on weight, on levity, on spring, on the resistance of fluid bodies and on the attractive and impulsive forces which form the basis of physics. But we must admit that these demonstrations are mechanical only, since the author himself admits at the end of page 4 and the beginning of page 5 [this is the sentence beginning "Wherefore the reader . . ." that I have quoted] that he has not considered the principles in question as a physicist, but purely as a geometer" and the reviewer goes on to find the same fault with the third book, saying that Newton proves that the tides can be accounted for by the attraction of the sun and moon, but he does not prove the attraction! I quote this because it shows two things, firstly that the greatness of the book was at once recognised and secondly how hard it was for Newton to get his point of view accepted. A review in the *Acta Eruditorum* (The Transactions of the Learned), produced at Leipzig, in Germany, runs to twelve pages and gives a careful account of what the book contains: it starts by calling Newton the foremost mathematician of the time.

The learned world, then, realised at once that here was a work of outstanding power, produced by a mastermind, but found it difficult to understand. It is probably true to say that fifty years had to pass before the Newtonian scheme was generally accepted and taught by men of science, let alone made the basis for further advances. The Scottish universities of St. Andrews and Edinburgh were probably the first to teach Newtonian science: at Cambridge itself, six years after the publication of the *Principia,* they were still teaching the Cartesian system, which was easy to understand. Even eminent mathematicians found the demonstrations in the *Principia* difficult: De Moivre, whose name is known, from his theorem, to all who study mathematics at the universities, found much of it beyond his comprehension at first reading, and therefore bought a copy which he tore into sheets and carried a few of them in his pocket at a time, so that he could study them whenever he had leisure.

The year after the appearance of the *Principia* there was general turmoil and confusion in the country, caused by the flight of James II. His interference with University affairs had already caused trouble in Cambridge and most people there, and probably elsewhere, were glad to see the last of him. Early in 1689 Newton was elected a Member of Parliament by the University, which, right up to 1948, had the right of electing a member, and served as such for about a year. This brought him often to London and may have had an important influence on his life. He made many new acquaintances, including that of John Locke, the great philosopher and a most attractive character, with whom he formed a firm friendship. He also met Pepys, who treated him with great respect and, no doubt, introduced him to various people of importance. The old course of his life was, then, much disturbed in different ways.

About this time Newton became very restless. It would seem that the production of the *Principia* had left him exhausted and that something of the old indifference to science, of which he had written to Hooke ten years earlier, had returned. He set about seeking an administrative job, but note that this was not because he was in want of money, as has sometimes been suggested. He was not badly off as Lucasian Professor and a Major Fellow of Trinity. While he was an M.P. various friends, probably at his request, certainly with his willing consent, tried to get him made Provost[1] of King's College, Cambridge, but without success. A little later, in 1691, he asked Locke to help him to get the post of Comptroller at the Mint, again without success. In the same year there was talk of obtaining for him the Mastership of the Charterhouse, but he did not think highly of this, writing to Locke, "I thank you for putting me in mind of Charterhouse, but I see nothing in it worth making a bustle for: besides a coach, which I consider not, it is but £200 per annum, with a confinement to the London air, and to such a way of living as I am not in love with; neither do I think it advisable to enter into such a competition as that would be for a better place." This is not quite the unworldly man that some have thought Newton to be.

In 1679 young Charles Montagu (who twenty years later became Lord Halifax) came to Trinity College and between him and Newton there began a lifelong friendship: "my intimate friend Mr. C. Montagu" wrote Newton in a letter to Halley. By the time of which we are speaking, 1691, Montagu had become a very influential man and Newton was relying on him to help him to a good post. Montagu did his

[1] King's College is one of the two Cambridge Colleges that do not call the Head of the College "Master." There is the Provost of King's College and the President of Queen's College.

best, but at the time nothing came of it. All these failures began to prey on Newton's mind and he fell into a period of great dejection and delusion, in which he thought that all his friends were failing him and deceiving him. At the beginning of 1692 he was writing such things as "Being convinced that Mr. Montagu is false to me, I have done with him" and somewhat later this melancholy and distrust became more serious. The next year he wrote to Pepys about his troubled state, saying that he had neither eaten nor slept well for a twelvemonth and that he must never see Pepys or the rest of his friends any more. He was, as we should say nowadays, clearly on the edge of a nervous breakdown. He even wrote to Locke, the kindest and most honourable of men, accusing him of making mischief. His feeling of being persecuted was evidently getting quite out of hand at the time. Locke sent him a very kindly and dignified answer, to which Newton replied that he had not slept for five nights and did not know what he was writing. It is clear, then, that Newton's health, temper and spirits were gravely disturbed and some writers have suggested that this was a period of madness from which he never recovered properly, that after this illness he lost his powers of grappling with scientific problems. However, Newton was never, even temporarily, what could be called insane and we shall see that his mental powers were not injured by this period of overstrain, sleeplessness and delusions of persecution. By the end of 1693 he seems to have recovered and become his normal self, but, as we have seen, his normal self was a highly-strung and morbidly sensitive man.

There is a silly story, first put out more than fifty years after his death, that he was driven mad by the loss of certain manuscripts, which were burnt because his little pet dog knocked over a candle on to them during his absence. The story is made more affecting by the description of how Newton did not beat the dog, but merely said, "Oh Diamond! Diamond! thou little knowst the mischief done." It is practically certain that Newton never had a dog; further, the only fire of which we have even a suggestion took place ten years before the period in question and then there was nothing of any special importance lost. In any case at the time of his nervous breakdown Newton was not interested in science—the papers are supposed to have had to do with scientific discoveries—but in obtaining an honourable and profitable administrative post. The story is not only baseless but quite out of keeping with the facts.

After his recovery Newton was closely engaged for a period in correspondence with the astronomer Flamsteed about the irregularities of the moon's motion, a correspondence which was marred by frequent quarrels and finally broken off in anger on both sides. Meanwhile Charles Montagu had been at work on Newton's behalf and in March 1696 wrote to him, "I am very glad that at last I can give you a good proof of my friendship, and the esteem the King has of your merits. Mr. Overton the Warden of the Mint, is made one of the Commissioners of the Customs, and the King has promised to make Mr. Newton Warden of the Mint. The office is most proper to you. 'Tis the chief officer in the Mint. 'Tis worth five or six hundred pounds per annum, and has not too much business to require more attendance than you can spare. . . ." So much for Newton's belief, during his derangement, that Montagu was playing him false.

Accordingly Newton went to London to become Warden of the Mint, which was actually the second post. The head was called Master of the Mint and Newton was duly promoted to this position in 1699. With the appointment to the Mint a new period of Newton's history begins, with a complete change in his mode of life.

VI

Life in London: The Opticks

WHEN NEWTON first came to live in London it appears that he accepted Charles Montagu's invitation to lodge near him but soon after he set up house on his own. Here we must introduce a witty and charming girl, Catherine Barton. Newton's mother had three children by her second husband, Barnabas Smith, one of whom, Hannah Smith, had married a Mr. Barton, like her father a clergyman. Catherine was the daughter of this marriage and was therefore Newton's niece. She came to keep house for him, probably as soon as he had a house to keep, when she would be about seventeen. By her wit and beauty she became very popular in London society. Jonathan Swift was a close friend and had genuine respect and affection for her. In particular, she grew to be on very intimate terms with Charles Montagu, and it was said by the scandal-mongers later that it was her influence with him that was responsible for Newton obtaining his post at the Mint, which was quite absurd, because when Newton obtained the post she must have been a country girl of fifteen, whom Montagu had probably never seen, and Montagu was already working on Newton's behalf long before this. After the death of Montagu (Lord Halifax, as he then was) in 1715 she married John Conduitt, who on Newton's death succeeded to his post at the Mint and who has left us valuable notes about Newton's life. Of the general household arrangements he says, "Sir Isaac lived in London ever since 1696, when he was made Warden of the Mint; nobody ever lived with him but my wife, who was with him nearly twenty years, before and after her marriage. He always lived in a very handsome generous manner, though without ostentation or vanity: always hospitable, and upon proper occasions, gave splendid entertainments." Other writers rather stress the "without ostentation" part of this account.

What has been said of Catherine Barton serves to show how Newton's outward life had changed, since she must have brought gay young people to his home, and, further, reminds us that Newton never married. It is, in fact, clear that women had no particular attrac-

tion for him. In his whole life there is no suggestion that he was ever even mildly in love,
except for a story that, when he was preparing
for Cambridge and lived with the Clarks at
Grantham, he fell in love with a step-daughter
of Clark's, Miss Storey, who was two years
younger than him and therefore not more than
sixteen at the time. The story is not very con-
vincing. It is entirely based, as far as I can make
out, on what Stukeley wrote down of what Miss
Storey (then Mrs. Vincent) told him when she
was a very old lady. "She says Sir Isaac was always a sober, silent, thinking lad, never was
known scarce to play with the boys abroad, but
would rather choose to be at home, even among
the girls. . . . Sir Isaac and she being thus
brought up together, it is said that Sir Isaac en-
tertained a passion for her when they grew up;
nor does she deny it"—not, you will note, nor
does *he* deny it, and Stukeley, who knew him
intimately, might well have asked him in his old
age. " 'Tis certain he always had a great kindness for her. He visited her whenever in the
country, in both her husband's days, and gave
her, at a time when it was useful to her, a sum
of money. She is a woman but of a middle stat-
ure, of a brisk eye, and without difficulty we
may discern she had been very handsome." This
is the sole record of a love affair in a very long
life, and, as for the visits and the present, New-

ton was always very generous with his money and always liked to meet friends of his youth or people from his part of the country. For instance, Stukeley tells us that he loved to attend the annual feasts held by Lincolnshire men in London and that on one occasion, late in Newton's life, there was such a feast at the *Ship* tavern, "When I went into the dining-room upstairs where the better sort of company was, it was talked that there was an old gentleman belowstairs whom they fancied to be Sir Isaac Newton. I instantly went down and finding it to be so, sat down with him. They above sent to desire us to walk up into the chief room. I answered, the chief room was where Sir Isaac Newton was. Upon which the upper room was immediately left to the ordinary company, and the better sort came to us." No early love affair is therefore necessary to account for Newton visiting the woman he had known when they were girl and boy if he happened to be in the neighbourhood where she lived.

Newton's work at the Mint, which he took very seriously, was of great importance, and, even if he had never touched science, he would still be known for it to those studying the history of the times, just as Pepys would be known to them for his work at the Admiralty even if he had never written a diary. The coinage of the country was in a very bad state. The standard

money was silver. Up to the time of Charles II
the coins were very thin and the edges were not
marked with the regular series of close lines,
called milling, found in modern silver, nor were
they round and smooth, as in the modern copper. The thin silver was cut with shears and
then stamped with the design. These old coins,
then, which were still in circulation in Newton's
time, were not exactly true to shape, size or
weight. It became a popular and profitable
fraud to clip little bits off the edge with shears
and the first clipping was followed by second
and further clippings, until, just before Newton
went to the Mint, the average shilling had been
reduced to half its weight. Some good money,
with proper edges that showed at once if the
coin had been tampered with, had been struck
not long before, but as the old money was still
in circulation, people hoarded the good money
and paid out the bad. Every paynight—Saturday
night in those days—there were prolonged disputes about the coins, since people objected,
very naturally, to receiving as shillings pieces
that were worth only sixpence. The poet Dry-
den, for instance, complains that his publisher,
on one occasion, sent him money so badly
clipped that he had to return it all. Montagu,
who was Chancellor of the Exchequer, and
so responsible for the matter, had prepared a
scheme for coinage of all the money, according

to which new milled money, of standard weight and metal, was to be produced and the old money called in and paid for at face value, the loss being borne by the State. A date was further fixed after which clipped money would not be accepted at all. It was Newton's task to take charge of the preparation of the new coins and the melting of the old. This was a matter that required great organising and business ability, as well as hard work. Newton showed at once that, far from being incompetent in worldly and administrative matters, he possessed the qualities necessary to make a success of the arduous task. A man may be a great scientist, and even absent-minded when engaged on strenuous research, and still be a very good organiser.

There were many difficulties, not only ones of machinery and finance. A blackguard, or let us say, as the historians do, a man of evil character, named Challoner, made attacks on Newton and his colleagues in order to cover certain criminal actions of his own, but was exposed and, in the end, hanged. "He was overthrown —no mean achievement for a don pitted against a clever criminal, with hostile politicians for a jury," says Sir John Craig, writing of this incident. There were various attempts to bribe Newton or to get him to resign his place, in which he was too efficient, too honest and too uncompromising to suit the unscrupulous, but these again were unsuccessful. Newton set up branch mints, such as one at Chester: he improved the machinery: he went into the question of all the operations of coinage, the speed of melting, the speed of the different kinds of machine, the number of hands required on each and the methods of finding the degree of purity of gold and silver. The weekly coinage rose, under his sway, from fifteen thousand pounds of metal per week to sixty thousand and finally to a hundred and twenty thousand pounds. By the middle of 1698 the great work of recoinage was practically over, the country mints were closed and the work dropped back to normal. The year after, within a day of his fifty-seventh birthday, Newton was raised to be Master of the Mint, the previous Master having just died. The Mastership was an extremely well paid post, which he continued to hold until his death. He carried out his work most efficiently, kept clear and exact records, got on very well with those both under him and above him and was, in every respect, an excellent civil servant who did not spare himself in attending to his duties. After the recoinage these duties, however, left him a fair amount of leisure.

In the years when he was busy with the recoinage Newton did little scientific work, but he retained his full powers. Shortly after his appointment to the Mint he received one afternoon a copy of two mathematical problems set by the celebrated Swiss mathematician Jean Bernoulli as a challenge to "the acutest mathematicians of the world." One of these problems was of peculiar difficulty at that time, requiring for its solution the calculus of variations, to which I have referred in talking of Book II of the *Principia*. Newton gave a copy of the solutions to Charles Montagu, who was at that time President of the Royal Society, on the next day: according to Conduitt he had worked them out before going to bed! When Newton's solutions were sent to Bernoulli, without Newton's name, he exclaimed that he knew the solver at once from the style in which the work was done—*tanquam ex ungue leonem,* as the lion is known by his claw.

In 1703 Newton was elected President of the Royal Society. He took a great interest in the affairs of the Society and remained President until his death in 1727. He was the first distinguished man of science to hold the office since Christopher Wren gave it up more than twenty years before: those who came in between were public figures like Pepys and Charles Montagu. In the same year another event took place which had an immediate effect on Newton— poor Hooke died, worn out and after prolonged suffering. Hooke's criticisms of his optical work had irritated Newton in the highest degree and it is believed that after the disputes in 1675 he had resolved to publish no more in this field while Hooke lived. In any case it was in 1704, the year after Hooke died, that he brought out his great work on light. It was called *Opticks: or a Treatise on the Reflexions, Refractions, Inflexions and Colours of Light,* and with it were bound two mathematical treatises on curves, written long before. In the Preface Newton says, "To avoid being engaged in Disputes about these Matters, I have hitherto delayed the printing, and should still have delayed it, had not the Importunity of Friends prevailed upon me." The *Opticks* is in English and the work on curves in Latin. As English was not much read on the Continent, and Latin was still the language of the learned, a Latin translation of the *Opticks* was made at Newton's request by Samuel Clarke and published two years later.

Newton starts the *Opticks* by insisting once more on his point of view, by making quite clear what it is that he sets out to accomplish. "My designs in this Book," he says, "is not to explain the Properties of Light by Hypotheses, but to propose and prove them by Reason and Experiment." Apparently it was still very difficult to make the reader accept this standpoint, for thirteen years later, in some very important new matter which he wrote for a new edition of the book, he said, "These Principles I con-

sider not as occult Qualities, supposed to result
from the specifick Forms of Things, but as general Laws of Nature, by which the Things themselves are form'd: *their Truth appearing to us
by Phaenomena, though their Causes be not yet
discover'd.*[1] For these are manifest Qualities
and their Causes only are occult. And the Aristotelians gave the Name of occult Qualities not
to manifest Qualities, but to such Qualities only
as they supposed to lie hid in Bodies, and to be
the unknown Causes of manifold Effects. . . .
To tell us that every Species of Things is en-
dow'd with an occult specifick Quality by which
it acts and produces manifest Effects is to tell
us nothing." For instance, to explain gravitational attraction by saying that it is due to an
innate striving of particles to be united is—to tell
us nothing. To say that hot bodies send out
light because the heat excites in them a luminous virtue which is expressed by radiant emis-
sion of a characteristic kind is—to tell us nothing. If we may judge by some of the explanations
which are swallowed to-day, not everybody yet
understands what Newton was trying to drive
home. He was saying that he would not speculate in matters that were beyond any possibility
of comparing with measurement, observation
and experiment; that he would not make guesses

---

[1] My italics, E. N. da C. A.

whose defence would merely be a matter of manipulating long words or appealing to prejudice. He did make hypotheses, and he called them so, in the *Principia,* but what he then meant by hypothesis was: I ask you to suppose so and so. If you accept it, so and so follows mathematically. These consequences are what we observe and measure, so my hypothesis is justified. This is quite different from saying that a body behaves in such a way because it is its nature to do so.

The first part of the book deals with the experiments on the prism, the coloured images produced by lenses and the reflecting telescope, matter already published, of which I have already said something. Newton gives a very exact account of how he polished the mirror of the telescope, which a London craftsman had failed to do to his satisfaction. He then proceeds to discuss colours such as we ordinarily observe— the colours of flowers, dyed stuffs and so on, which are, of course, not pure spectral colours. The colour of a red book or a red rose is not a pure spectral red, and brown is not a spectral colour at all. Newton proved that all colours are produced by mixtures of pure spectral colours. A piece of pure red cloth looks red because it absorbs the whole blue end and the green, yellow and orange part of the spectrum, but lets the red go out again: if we illuminate it with blue light it looks quite black, because there is no red light for it to throw back. Often, however, the coloured body absorbs certain wide regions of the spectrum, and lets the others go: a red body may absorb the whole blue end up to and including the green, but leave a good part of the yellow and orange unabsorbed. Such a body will look a different kind of red to the eye according to the amount of orange and yellow. A brown body absorbs strongly, but not completely, light of all colours except the orange, of which it absorbs very little: the light which it throws back when white light falls on it is therefore orange, with an admixture of a certain amount of all the other spectral colours. A purple body absorbs the middle colours of the spectrum and throws back red and blue. The colours of flowers and cloths and paints are therefore called absorption or subtraction colours; they are due to the colours which the surface subtracts from the light that falls on it, and so their colour depends on the nature of this light. If we project a big spectrum and put a bright red poppy in the red part, it will look bright red: in the orange part it will look orange, but not so bright: probably it will show rather feeble yellow in the yellow: but in the rest of the spectrum it will look black, since there it completely absorbs the light to which it is exposed. Ordinary artificial light from a hot-wire electric lamp, say, is not quite of the same spectral make-up as sunlight, being comparatively weak at the blue and violet end of the spectrum. Hence coloured fabrics, especially those with much blue in them, look a different colour by sunlight and by ballroom light, as every woman knows.

It is now easy to understand why mixed paints give quite different colours from mixed lights. Yellow and blue paints or powders mixed give green, because the yellow absorbs the red and blue and throws back yellow with a good deal of the neighbouring green and orange: the blue absorbs the red, orange and yellow, but throws back blue, with some of the neighbouring green and violet. The only colour that escapes the two absorptions together is therefore green. But a patch of blue light and a patch of yellow light overlapping on a white screen, which throws them both back, produce a colour effect something near white—rather pink than green. The problems of colour vision are very complicated and difficult, since the behaviour of the eye to colour has to be taken into account as well as the physics of light. For instance, while the skilled ear can detect the separate notes in a musical chord, the most skilled eye cannot tell the difference between white light made up of all spectral colours and a white light which can be produced by the careful blending of three chosen spectral colours. Newton recognised this difficulty and pointed out further that, for instance, a blow on the eye may cause a fire-coloured flash to be seen and that colour sensations can be produced by pressing the eye. He was the first to explain how the colours of material bodies are related to the spectrum and are a consequence of the compound nature of white light, which he had proved; he was the first to make plain the difference between subtraction colours and addition colours and the first to attempt a scientific study of the perception of colour in general.

He also clearly explained the colours of the rainbow, as due to the bending (or refraction, as it is called) of light which penetrates into minute raindrops and, after reflection inside the drop, comes out again with a second refraction: the refraction by the water is accompanied by a separation of colours, just as is refraction by the glass prism. Owing to overlapping, the rainbow colours are not pure spectral colours. Newton further showed that the second bow sometimes seen outside the brighter, ordinary, one is due to two reflexions within the drop. Descartes had earlier given a general explanation of the rainbow in terms of refraction by water drops, but Newton took the matter much further.

Then we have the treatment of the colours of thin plates, such as soap bubbles or flakes of mica, and of the colours shown by the thin air film enclosed when a slightly curved lens face is pressed on to a flat plate of glass, colours known as "Newton's rings." In the past I have occasionally seen a little system of Newton's rings wandering over the screen in a cinematograph, due, of course, to a slight lack of adjustment in the projection lenses, but that does not often happen nowadays. To explain these colours of thin plates Newton gave to light certain wave properties, as I have already said. The reason that he did not accept light altogether as a wave motion was that, as he pointed out, if a travelling wave comes to a screen with a hole in it, the part that goes through the hole should spread out after passing through. This happens, for instance, with long sea waves coming to the entrance of a harbour made by stone walls. The wave system that gets through the opening does not form a straight pathway, but spreads out sideways, forming a kind of triangle with a blunt point at the entrance. Now, said Newton, light travels in straight lines and when it goes through a hole forms a sharp beam: it does not spread out. However, if the hole, or opening, is very small, there *is* a sideways spreading, which is greater for red than for blue light, so that colour effects are produced. You can see them if you look at the filament of an electric lamp through a very fine handkerchief. The spreading out can only be seen with very fine openings because the wave length of light is very small. Newton had actually carried out experiments with a very fine slit which showed these effects, but, strangely enough, he missed their great significance. There are many other things of the greatest importance in the book, but a fairly deep knowledge of physics is required to appreciate them. As a record of experiment, and scientific deduction from experiment, the *Opticks* is supreme. Perhaps enough has been said here to indicate how wide is the field that it covers.

Probably all the work described in the *Opticks* was done before Newton came to London. He says in the Preface that, as we know, part was written in 1675, and that much of the rest was added about twelve years later—that is, just after the *Principia* was completed—while the last part of the book was "put together out of scattered papers." The book is therefore not proof that he had thought hard and long on scientific matters after he took over work at the Mint. However, to the second edition, which came out in 1717, he made some very remarkable additions which must have been the result of recent thought and prove that his powers were in no way diminished, when he cared to exert them. He set them down as "Queries" at the end of the book, probably because they are rather more speculative than his usual scientific writings, but it must not be thought that they are just questions. They are adventures in scientific thought, discussions of possibilities: two of them, Queries 25 and 26, which deal with polarised light and give the essence of the explanation of its most striking behaviour, cover more than eight pages, and the last Query, number 31, runs to thirty-one pages. Among the remarkable things which it contains is the suggestion that the forces that hold atoms—"the small particles of bodies," he calls them—together may be electrical. The only kind of electricity known in those days was that produced by rubbing such bodies as amber and glass, but Newton says, "perhaps electrical Attraction may reach to such small distances, even without being excited by Friction." He also suggests that it may be through these forces that matter acts on light. There was no serious attempt to explain atomic actions by electric forces, which we now know to be the right way, until about a hundred years later. At the Newton celebrations of 1946, Academician S. I. Vavilov, now dead, who was at the time President of the Academy of Sciences of the U.S.S.R. (Soviet Russia), communicated an address on *Newton and the Atomic Theory,* in which he refers to the words just quoted as showing Newton's "extraordinary intuition in conjecturing the main features of natural phenomena, without going into details and the more complicated problems," and quotes another passage of which he says that "these words could be used in full, and without any alteration whatsoever, as the motto for any work of to-day on the structure of matter." He also refers with admiration to a little paper, *De Natura Acidorum* (On the nature of Acids), by Newton, which was published in 1710 in a kind of technical encyclopædia, and was probably written, more or less as notes, at about the same time as the Query 31.

At the time when the *Opticks* appeared Newton's glory was recognised throughout the scientific world. In 1705 Queen Anne and her whole court, including her husband the Prince Consort, George of Denmark, who was interested in science and had been elected a Fellow of the Royal Society the year before, visited Cambridge, and made this the occasion of conferring a knighthood on Newton at Trinity College. He was not knighted for his services at the Mint but for his services to science, for the Queen knew something of his merits and is said to have declared that she thought it a happiness to have lived at the same time as, and to have known, so great a man. From that date on he was a national figure, wondered at and respected in all circles. The knighthood was not, of course, the cause of this regard, but such an honour had never been conferred before for achievements in pure science and it came as a clear sign and expression of the respect in which Newton was held.

VII

Old Age

AT THE time when he was knighted Newton was sixty-two and had another twenty-two years of life before him. During this period he made no great scientific discoveries nor, indeed, did he devote any large part of his thought to new scientific problems, although, as I have already pointed out, he was still capable of solving mathematical questions of the greatest difficulty, of profound suggestions and of daring and inspired speculations that seemed to foretell the scientific future.

His time was fully occupied. He had his work at the Mint and he took a great interest in the affairs of the Royal Society, which, on account of prolonged quarrels, among other things, required considerable attention. He was present at nearly every one of the Society's weekly meetings. Before he was made President the meeting day was Wednesday, but, that being the Mint's day for paying out coin, it was changed to Thursday for Newton's convenience, and has remained Thursday ever since. Newton was also concerned with new editions of his books and with, alas, the usual disputes. Further, as we shall see, he had many interests outside science and Mint matters which took up much of his time and effort.

As regards disputes, troubles with Flamsteed continued. Flamsteed had made long and accurate observations on the moon, which Newton needed for his theory of the disturbances of the moon's motion by the sun, and their dealings about these matters soon led to bickerings in which Halley was involved. Both Newton and Flamsteed were difficult men, particularly Flamsteed—but certainly not only Flamsteed. He generally spoke of Newton's powers with great respect, but he did not at all relish Newton's way of dealing with him and his work, neither was he very tactful, to say the least. Two examples, from letters of his, may be sufficient. Newton had given him a copy of his *Opticks,* and he records, "I thanked him for his book: he said that he hoped I approved it. I told him truly, no." In the first year of Newton's presidency of the Royal Society he wrote, "Our Society decays and produces nothing remarkable, nor is it like to do it, I fear, while 'tis governed by persons that either value nothing but their own interests, or understand little but vegetables [he meant Sir Hans Sloane, the Secretary], and how, by making a bouncing noise, to cover their own ignorance." On the other hand, Newton, having persuaded Prince George, the Consort, to bear the cost of printing Flamsteed's great astronomical book, proceeded with the work in a very highhanded fashion, more or less without consulting Flamsteed's wishes or interest. Further, very meanly, in the second edition of the *Principia* he left out many passages in which, in the first edition, he had acknowledged Flamsteed's services. It is a melancholy story, but it is not right to hide this side of Newton's character. Great men, even very great men, are not perfect.

The other main source of trouble was Leibniz. I have mentioned the disputes which arose as to whether Leibniz had invented the differential calculus by himself or whether he had somehow heard of Newton's work and borrowed from him. These disputes reached some violence but had died down soon after Newton came to London. With the publication of the *Opticks* the whole affair flamed up again more violently than ever. As you know, two mathematical papers were printed at the end of the book, and in the preface Newton said that years ago he had lent out a manuscript of these papers and implied that Leibniz had copied from it. Unseemly accusations were made by the friends of both great men and in 1712, eight years after the *Opticks,* a book was issued by the Royal Society which went into the whole question and concluded very much against Leibniz. There is no doubt that Newton had actively concerned himself with this book and was largely responsible for it, and for a second edition that came out ten years later. The book was certainly not altogether fair, and led to a great deal of bitterness on the Continent, including an attack in which Newton's injustice to Hooke and Flamsteed was brought up. Leibniz had at first admitted that Newton's discovery had been before, and quite independent of, his own, but, after all the attacks on him, he in his turn suggested that Newton had borrowed from him. The troubles died down with the death of Leibniz in 1716, but for twelve years they had irritated Newton, taken up his time and embittered his life. Nobody comes well out of the investigations which learned men have been making into the affair ever since. It is a very wearisome and unpleasant history, which was a matter of grave concern to Newton in his old age.

Let us turn to pleasanter matters. During

visits to Cambridge at about the time he was knighted Newton had seen a good deal of his friend Bentley, who had been made Master of Trinity. Bentley had studied the *Principia* and urged Newton to bring out a second edition of the book: in fact he provided the prodding that was always necessary before the great man would face publication. Newton had made many notes and worked out new points concerning the theory of gravitation, but he was unwilling to attend to the wearisome details of bookmaking. Luckily a brilliant and amiable young man named Roger Cotes was found who could both understand the work and get on well with Newton, for whom he had the profoundest admiration. The relations between the two men were of the pleasantest and show Newton at his best. In general he was kind, considerate and generous to young men who were serious students of his work and who sought him out, but Cotes was his favourite and he had the highest opinion of his abilities. Cotes completed his work as editor, but died not long after, at the early age of thirty-three. He had already done important scientific work of his own. Newton said of him, "If Mr. Cotes had lived we might have known something," which from such a man was high praise indeed.

The second edition of the *Principia* appeared in 1713, with an excellent preface by Cotes, in which he defends the "new principle," as he calls it, of founding science on experiment and observation. In particular, he refers to people who disliked the Newtonian mechanics of the heavens because it contradicted the opinions of Descartes, and explains and praises with dignified enthusiasm the methods of the *Principia*. So it is evident that there were still plenty of learned men who were unconvinced of the significance of Newton's work. At the end of the preface Cotes mentions that copies of the first edition were very scarce and fetched a high price, which was why Bentley "by frequent entreaties and almost by chidings" had persuaded the author to allow this new edition to appear. The book contains new matter about the resistance of fluids and about the motions of the heavenly bodies, in particular those of the moon and comets, as well as some new experiments about the motion of liquids.

This demand for the *Principia* grew steadily, as its importance became more widely realised. Two issues of the work appeared in Amsterdam, one in 1714 and one in 1723, and in this latter year the printing of a third edition began in England. This time Newton chose another young man to help with the revision of the work and to see it through the press, Henry Pemberton. Once more, he showed great kindness to his assistant and in return received unbounded admiration. The book came out in 1726, the last edition in Newton's lifetime. After that it was, of course, frequently reprinted in the original Latin—in particular there were two fine Swiss editions—and translated into foreign languages. An English translation first appeared shortly after Newton's death and has been often reprinted in England and America; a French translation came thirty years later; a German translation in 1872; and in the present century the book has appeared in Italian, Russian and Swedish. This is, perhaps, some little sign of the regard in which it was and is held and of the interest still taken in it.

Other books, written by Newton long before, came out in his old age. I have mentioned the *De Analysi,* the mathematical treatise, so important for the calculus, of which Newton gave Barrow a hand-written copy shortly after his Woolsthorpe period. This was first printed in 1711, with other mathematical works: as usual Newton left the job of editing and bringing out the book in other hands. A few years before there appeared a book by Newton called *Arithmetica Universalis,* of which an English translation came out later as *Universal Arithmetic:* it was edited and published by William Whiston, who had the usual trouble in getting Newton's permission to print. You must not be misled by the title: it was not an arithmetic in the present day use of the word, but mainly a treatise on algebra, containing many original discoveries of first importance. One of the most striking is a certain rule about equations, stated without proof, for which a proof was finally supplied, about a hundred and sixty years later, by the great mathematician Sylvester. Then, again, just after Newton's death appeared a book, *Optical Lectures,* which was translated from the Latin copy of the lectures on optics which he gave at Cambridge in 1669, sixty years earlier! The preface tells the usual story of how he proposed to publish the lectures, but gave up the intention on account of disputes. The original Latin lectures, complete, came out the year after the English, which is a translation of the first part only. The only translation of the whole Latin book into a modern language that I know of is one into Russian, which appeared in 1946.

If I detain you with these books it is because the whole business is so characteristic of Newton, that in his old age work which he did as a young man should be appearing, with his rather grudging consent, for the first time in print. Newton himself did not spend much time either on them or on the editions of the *Principia* to which I have referred. He left the main work, as we have seen, to others. The writings with which he occupied himself in his old age and on which he spent great effort are ones of which we either know little or of which little is thought to-day. They deal with Biblical matters and theology and with the fixing of dates in ancient history.

Newton had been keenly interested in religious matters in the prime of his life and onwards. How much time he spent on them when he was most active in science is hard to say, because it is hard to know what reliance can be placed on various statements that have been made. For instance, his friend, John Craig, a distinguished but somewhat eccentric mathematician (he calculated the ratio of the happiness promised in another world to that which can be obtained in this), says that he was much more concerned with his inquiries into religion than into science, and that the reason that he showed the errors in Descartes' scheme was that he thought it was used as a foundation for disbelief. This is, perhaps, an exaggeration, but there is undoubtedly some basis for it. Soon after writing the *Principia* Newton was heavily engaged in writing about the scriptures and religious opinions and in 1691 he was carrying on an active correspondence with John Locke on such matters as the prophecies of Daniel. A brief work entitled *Historical Account of Two Notable Corruptions of the Scriptures,* printed long after his death, was probably written about this time. In a very large collection of papers

that descended to the Earl of Portsmouth from
Newton's grandniece are about a million and
a half words—say enough to fill fifty books the
size of this—on religious and historical matters.
There are also about half a million words on alchemical matters, to which I shall refer in the
next chapter. Some of them may be passages
copied out of books, but in any case this is
sufficient to show how much time and attention Newton spent on such things. Much was
undoubtedly written when Newton was round
about fifty, but much also may be set down to
his old age.

Two books were published on the historical
and religious part of Newton's work. The one
that appeared during his lifetime led to a fresh
series of troubles. Some time in his seventies
Newton wrote a manuscript on chronology, that
is, on dating the events of early history, Biblical, Greek, Egyptian, Assyrian and so on. The
scheme is said to have been drawn up in his
Cambridge days, but the properly written account was prepared for the Princess of Wales,
who had been discussing education with the old
man. As usual, it was not for publication. A
written copy got to France and, by a breach of
faith, fell into the hands of a bookseller, who,
after trying to get permission, but obtaining no
answer at all to his letters, published it. Criticism
was aroused, the exasperated Newton replied

and the reply gave rise to new attacks. The full and amended work which was now prepared by Newton for publication appeared in the year after his death, under the title, *The Chronology of the Ancient Kingdoms Amended*. I am afraid that no one reads it nowadays or would take it very seriously if they did. Newton thought that he could not be more than twenty years wrong with any of his dates: modern opinion is that he was often wrong by centuries. But it is clear that he spent immense trouble on the work in his last years.

The other book was called *Observations on the Prophecies of Daniel and the Apocalypse of St. John* and came out after his death. It is clear that it cost him prodigious labour. The kind of thing he was concerned with was trying to connect the prophecies with subsequent history: for instance the beast in Daniel has ten horns and there came up among them a little horn. Newton identified these horns with kingdoms, and decided that the little horn was the Roman Church. He shows deep learning in his careful account of the early history of the Church.

We have now glanced at some of the matters that occupied the end of Newton's life and we see that science was not prominent among them. He had become a great figure in the world, received with friendship by the royal family; revered by the scientific world, young and old, with the few exceptions who have been mentioned; welcomed with respect wherever he went, whether among the aristocracy, the Cambridge dons or plain folk from his countryside; sought out by all distinguished foreigners who visited the country. He was the ruler of the Royal Society. He was a wealthy man and if he lived plainly it was entirely at his own wish. At his death he left nearly £32,000, a huge sum in those days.

As for his personal appearance, he was grey when under forty and white-haired soon after, rather short, strong, sinewy and well made. In his later life he became stout. In youth and manhood he was somewhat near-sighted, with the consequence that in old age, when sight becomes longer, his sight was excellent; Stukeley says that he saw Newton, when he was eighty-two, add up the accounts of the Royal Society without spectacles and without writing materials. His hearing was excellent: further, to the day of his death he had, we are told, lost only one tooth. He kept his hair too, as white as silver in his old age: when his wig was off—it was the custom to wear full curly wigs in those days —he was a venerable sight. His face was pink and fresh. All this points to a man of remarkable vitality, which was, no doubt, preserved by his temperate habits in food, drink and all matters.

Accounts of his general attitude and expression vary. Bishop Atterbury says that in his whole face and make-up nothing of his penetrating wisdom appeared and that he had something rather languid in his look and manner. Conduitt says that he had a very lively and piercing eye: Stukeley that his countenance indicated vast penetration. These are very contradictory descriptions. The truth probably is that his expression varied greatly according to whether he was tired or fresh, interested or bored, angry or content, thinking or relaxing, in formal dress or at his ease. Stukeley and Conduitt were intimate friends; how well the Bishop knew him I do not know. The portraits in his old age vary, some, especially those in formal dress, with wig, show a dignified and benevolent but not particularly striking expression: one, painted of him without wig when he was in his middle sixties, shows a keenly intelligent, penetrating and rather hostile look.

Except for an attack of illness during his Cambridge days and for the long period of sleeplessness at the time of his nervous breakdown after writing the *Principia,* he enjoyed remarkably good health until he was entering his eightieth year, when he was attacked by a painful illness from which he temporarily recovered. After that his health was never good and he was forced to live very quietly. He was stricken with gout and other troubles. When he was eighty-three he began to suffer from inflammation of the lungs and was persuaded to leave the smoke of London and live in the fresh air of the village of Kensington. Londoners may be surprised to hear Kensington, now swallowed up in a London which stretches for miles beyond it, described as a village, but so it was in those days.[1] Stukeley gives a charming description of the two of them drinking tea together in the garden there on a warm April afternoon.

In February 1727 he went to London, something of a journey in a coach, to preside at a meeting of the Royal Society. The fatigue and shaking—roads were rough in those days—proved too much for him and when he returned to Kensington he was very ill and never recovered. He died on March 20, retaining his faculties to the end.

The greatest honours were paid to him at his funeral. His body lay in state, like that of a sovereign, in a chamber adjoining Westminster Abbey and he was buried in the Abbey itself, with every ceremony. In the funeral procession the pall was supported by the Lord High Chancellor, two dukes and three earls. The place allotted for his grave and the monument afterwards

---

[1] A picture of Burlington House in those days shows Piccadilly as a country road with farm wagons going along it.

built over it was one that had often been refused to the greatest of the nobility, and in those days the great nobles usually got their own way. The monument itself, which is worth a visit to-day, is an imposing piece of work. Among those present at the funeral was the great French writer Voltaire, who afterwards wrote a popular book on Newton's discoveries which did much to spread his fame in France. No Englishman of science, art or letters has, either before or since, received such extraordinary marks of respect on his death.

VIII

Newton the Man

I HAVE tried to give in simple words an account
of what Newton achieved in science and to convince you of its astonishing originality, scope
and importance. Of how he arrived at his great
discoveries we understand very little. It is pretty
clear that they did not come to him in the form
in which he finally set them down. William
Whiston, who knew him well, and uttered some
very hard things about his character, was convinced that he had the power of perceiving
scientific truths before he had proved them. Let
us look at what he wrote. "Sir Isaac, in mathematics, could sometimes see almost by intuition,
even without demonstration" and he then gives
a mathematical example, after which he con-
tinues, "And when he did but propose conjectures in natural philosophy, he almost always

knew them to be true at the same time; and yet did this Sir Isaac Newton compose a *Chronology,* and wrote out eighteen copies of its first and principal chapter with his own hand, but little different one from another, which proved no better than a sagacious romance." I have given examples of things that he set down without proof in the *Principia* and elsewhere which were not shown to be true until much later, and of his anticipation of modern theories. Even the conclusions that he sets down in the *Principia* with such systematic proof by geometrical methods were probably not first reached by those methods. It is possibly true that all very great men of science have a power of, as it were, smelling out the truth, divining what is behind scientific appearances: they do not argue things out to begin with in the nice, clean, tidy manner in which they afterwards present their findings to the world. Newton, perhaps, possessed this power of scientific foresight, correct scientific surmise, to a greater extent than any other man.

It is little use discussing Newton in terms of ordinary experience, because he was a quite extraordinary man. Other great men of science, such as Faraday, Hertz and Rutherford, have devoted all their best labours to their scientific researches. Newton had long periods when he seems to have been indifferent to science, not only after the *Principia* but before it, as when, at the age of thirty-six, he wrote to Hooke that his affection to philosophy was worn out. In fact, we can say, without going far wrong, that his energies were devoted more or less equally to four pursuits: exact science; administration at the Mint; religious matters; and chemistry and alchemy. I have said a good deal about the first two—if I have said less about the third it is not because Newton necessarily thought less about it. In the library which he left at his death the works of the early writers on Christianity, the so-called "Church Fathers," were prominent; there were a large number of other works on religion and a dozen different copies of the Bible. Theology and divinity—the close, systematic, philosophical study of religion—occupied some of his best attention and he was deeply learned in this field. I have already referred to his great knowledge of scriptural matters and his profound interest in the prophecies of Daniel. He was a very serious and scrupulous man, and it seems likely, from what we know of his beliefs, that he could not conscientiously agree to all of the thirty-nine articles of faith of the Church of England, especially those that concern the Trinity, and that that is why he never could or would take Holy Orders.

This brings us to alchemy, which is, perhaps, even more difficult to discuss. Alchemy was the craft of chemical changes of various kinds, as pursued before chemistry developed into a science of the modern kind. This it began to do with the work of Robert Boyle, who was a friend of Newton's: his numerous books were in Newton's library. Alchemy was closely connected with attempts to change base metals into gold: the "philosopher's stone," which the alchemists sought, was supposed to be at the same time the means by which this change, or transmutation, could be carried out and a universal medicine. There were among the alchemists many swindlers and charlatans who boasted that they could make precious metals and who, by one means or another, obtained money from the credulous. There is a very amusing account of a cheating alchemist and how he carried out an experiment that seemed to change mercury into silver in Chaucer's *Canon's Yeoman's Tale.* For other alchemists, serious and honourable men, the transmutation of metals had a mystic meaning and was not thought of mainly as a source of profit. These philosophical alchemists, seeing that man was a combination of a material body and an immaterial soul and mind, believed that all matter had a kind of life and a kind of spirit. They believed in the power of signs and symbols. They thought of metals as breeding, like living beings, in the earth: some of them certainly believed in magic, all were convinced that chemical changes were part of one great mystery, connecting heaven and earth, matter and mind. The supposed connection between heavenly bodies and human life is at the basis of astrology, which in some ways was akin to alchemy. A secret brotherhood called the Rosicrucians believed in the magic side of alchemy, mixing religion, disembodied spirits and chemistry in a curious way. The books of the Rosicrucians were among the hundred or so chemical, alchemical and mystical books in Newton's library.

Newton undoubtedly devoted much time and energy to chemical experiment. His interest, very likely, began when as a boy he was lodging in a chemist's shop, and continued when he was at Cambridge. Newton's concern with metals and alloys—consider, for example, his telescope mirror—would also lead him to alchemical books, where much practical knowledge of these matters was preserved. Soon after he published his first work on light, a mathematical friend, in a letter to Gregory, remarked that he had not troubled Newton lately because the great man had lost interest in mathematics and was spending all his time on chemistry. At the time when he was writing the *Principia,* for six weeks in the spring and six weeks in the autumn he kept his chemical furnaces going continually. "What his aim might be I was not able to penetrate into," writes Humphrey Newton, who was with him at the time and records the immense trouble he took with these chemical experiments. I have already mentioned the great quantity of manuscripts on chemical and alchemical matters that he left behind him, which has never been properly examined. He wrote to Boyle, who had alchemical interests, letters on a theory of attractions and chemical combination, conjectures of which he says, "For my own part, I have so little fancy to things of this nature, that had not your encouragement moved me to it, I should never, I think, have thus far set pen to paper about them," a typical Newton remark.

Nevertheless, his interest in this type of chemical theory continued and in his final "Queries" in the *Opticks* he brings it in. Nobody really knows what Newton was after in his chemical researches: he never refers in his published writings to his alchemical interests and hardly to his chemical experiments. Not that when I use the words 'chemical' and 'alchemical' I mean to suggest that the two can be separated in Newton's work: what I do mean to suggest is that there were two aspects of his work, a material and a mystical, an ancient and a modern. There are some extraordinary passages in his letters and notes on the subject, as when he writes, concerning the possibility of transmuting metals to gold, that it "has been thought fit to be concealed by others that have known it, and therefore may possibly be an inlet to something more noble, not to be communicated without immense danger to the world, if there should be any verity in the Hermetic writers." The Hermetic philosophers were those who dealt with, among other things concerning matter and spirit, the mystic side of alchemy: the word comes from Hermes Trismegistus, who was regarded as the founder of the occult sciences. "Immense danger to the world" the transmutation of the elements has proved to involve, in the atomic bomb.

Little can be said about the reason and results of Newton's chemical experiments, for little is known. What is certain is that they formed an important part of his life, that he devoted some of his best attention to them. Remember always how secretive Newton was, especially about anything that concerned his inner life. After all, had things fallen out a little differently we might never have known anything about his great scientific work except from the letters and notes of people living at the time.

As for Newton's character, it was strangely mixed. He was capable, as we have seen, of very ungenerous, one might almost say spiteful, actions, when his scientific priority and supremacy seemed to be in any way questioned, but at the same time his behaviour to young men was free from all arrogance and charmed them. He could often speak very modestly of his own achievements. Shortly before his death he said, "I do not know what I may appear to the world; but to myself I seem to have been only like a boy, playing on the seashore, and diverting myself in now and then finding a smoother pebble or a prettier shell than ordinary, while the great ocean of truth lay all undiscovered before me." We can explain this, perhaps, by supposing that Newton's aim was to understand the whole scheme and mystery of the world, in which he believed that the truths of exact science were only a part of a greater truth. His religious and mystic interests would fit in with this suggestion.

We admit that he was very easily irritated, and that when irritated he was liable to become petty. A man of his powers and nature may be allowed to be irritable, especially when overworked. There is, however, not much justification for writing of him as the poet Cowper did:

> *Patient of contradiction as a child,*
> *Affable, humble, diffident and mild,*
> *Such was Sir Isaac.*

Presumably Cowper had never heard of Hooke, Flamsteed or Leibniz.

His horror of any kind of controversy, his dislike for publication because it might lead to dispute is another strange feature. I know of no other great man of science to compare with him in this, although I have, of course, known men, great and small, who did not like being contradicted. It is, perhaps, all part of his shrinking from intimacy with the outside world; although he could and would converse freely and affably, he never seems to have taken anybody into his confidence.

He was not indifferent to money: he was careful with his investments and left a large fortune. He did not, however, attach too much importance to it and was always very generous, giving away quite large sums without thought or hesitation. When bank notes of high value were stolen from his pocket, and he was asked how much he had lost, he merely said, "Too much." And when he was tricked into giving too much for an estate, he refused to prosecute, saying that he would not go to law to prove he had made a fool of himself. He was not without a certain dry humour. Stukeley says that although he was of a very serious frame of mind, he had often seen him laugh, but I have only read of one occasion when he seems to have been thoroughly amused. Humphrey Newton tells that he lent a friend a copy of Euclid's geometry and later inquired of him what progress he had made and how he liked it. Whereupon the friend asked Newton what use and benefit in life that kind of study would be to him. "Upon which

Sir Isaac was very merry." I do not expect all business men to understand the joke.

Well, there is this extraordinary man, of the world yet not of the world; supreme in the exact sciences but a mystic at heart; high-minded and petty; modest and overbearing; suspicious, sensitive and shrinking, but a good man of affairs; arousing admiration, respect and reverence, but no warm human affection. A man who mixed freely with other men of different birth, of different temperaments and pursuits, but always a man withdrawn, guarding, in the ultimate, his own secrets as to what he believed and what he was above all seeking: a man revealing great mysteries of nature's machinery but reticent about much which he had profoundly pondered: the first modern scientist and the last of the mages.

Do not think that too much has, in this book, been claimed for Newton. The greatest minds in science that have come after him, from Laplace to Einstein, write in whole-hearted admiration of the work of this supreme thinker. In the modern world we have, of course, gone far beyond what Newton did, but he supplied the foundations on which all since him have built, he discovered the method and will ever remain as the supreme example of the power of the human mind to bring order into our observations of the ways of the material universe.

Note on the Retrograde Motion of the Planets

WE TAKE as an example Mars. It must be remembered that what is in question is the direction in which the planet is seen from the earth, for, if the earth be considered stationary, this is what tells us how the planet is moving.

In the diagram the outer circle represents the orbit of Mars and the inner circle that of the earth. The actual orbits are not quite circular, but circles suffice for the present purpose. To go round its orbit Mars takes 1 year 322 days, so that while the earth traverses its compete orbit Mars is tracing out not much more than half its orbit.

ab, cd, ef are pairs of positions of the earth, and *AB, CD, EF* are corresponding positions of Mars, the direction of Mars as seen from the earth being shown by the arrows. While the earth goes from *a* to *b* the direction of the arrow *aA* moves in the anti-clockwise direction to *bB:* Mars is going forward, as shown by the arrow between the circles. While, however, the earth goes from *c* to *d* the direction of the arrow *cC* moves in the clockwise direction to *dD:* Mars is going backwards. While the earth goes from *e* to *f* the direction of the arrow *eE* moves to *fF* in the anti-clockwise direction: Mars is going forward again.

In the positions between *b* and *c* shown by the

broken arrows the direction of Mars does not change: the planet appears to be stationary while

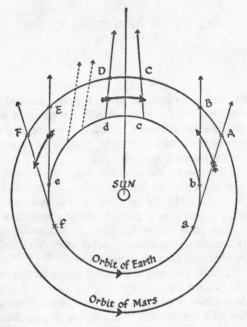

Fig. 6.

reversing its direction of motion from forwards to backwards.

This apparent retrograde motion was the great complication that confronted the astronomers who considered the earth to be stationary.

Chronological Table

Some events in Newton's Life		Some events in British and general History	
1642	Isaac Newton born at Woolsthorpe.	1642	Galileo dies.
1661	Enters Trinity College, Cambridge.	1660	Restoration of Charles II. Royal Society founded.
1665-7	At Woolsthorpe lays foundations of his great discoveries.	1665-6	Great Plague.
		1665-7	Second Dutch War.
		1668	Peace of Aix-la-Chapelle.
1669	Appointed Lucasian Professor of Mathematics.	1678	Peace of Nijmwegen.
		1683	Siege of Vienna.
1672	First paper published by Royal Society. Elected Fellow of the Royal Society.	1685	Accession of James II.
		1688	Abdication of James II.
		1689	Accession of William and Mary.
1684	Halley's visit to Cambridge which led to *Principia*.	1691	Robert Boyle dies.

CHRONOLOGICAL TABLE

Some events in Newton's Life		*Some events in British and general History*	
1687	*Principia* published.	1702	Accession of Queen Anne.
1689	Elected M.P. for Cambridge University.	1703	Battle of Blenheim. Robert Hooke dies.
1692-3	Nervous breakdown.	1707	Union of England and Scotland.
1696	Warden of the Mint.	1714	Accession of George I.
1699	Master of the Mint.	1716	Leibniz dies.
1703	Elected President of Royal Society.	1723	Christopher Wren dies.
1704	*Opticks* published.	1725	Treaty of Vienna.
1705	Knighted.	1727	Accession of George II.
1713	*Principia* second edition.		
1717	*Opticks* second edition.		
1727	Dies at Kensington.		

INDEX

04G

SCIENCE STUDY SERIES